JH

Aim for a stellar Physics mark with CGP!

Edexcel 9-1 International GCSE Physics is no picnic, and that's putting it mildly. Luckily, we've squeezed all the facts, theory and practical skills you'll need into this CGP book — plus exam practice questions to put your Physics knowledge to the test.

It's great for the Edexcel International GCSE Science Double Award too!

How to access your free Online Edition

This book includes a free Online Edition to read on your PC, Mac or tablet.
To access it, just go to **cgpbooks.co.uk/extras** and enter this code...

2447 1495 3778 5073

By the way, this code only works for one person. If somebody else has used this book before you, they might have already claimed the Online Edition.

CGP — still the best! ☺

Our sole aim here at CGP is to produce the highest quality books —
carefully written, immaculately presented and dangerously close to being funny.

Then we work our socks off to get them out to you
— at the cheapest possible prices.

Contents

Section 7 — Radioactivity and Particles

Section 8 — Astrophysics

Describing Experiments

Paper 2

Paper 2

This book covers both Physics Paper 1 and Physics
Paper 2 material. Some material is needed for Paper 2 only —
we've clearly marked this in green boxes.
The Paper 2 revision questions in the book are also printed in green.
If you're doing a Science (Double Award) qualification
you don't need to learn the Paper 2 material.

Published by CGP.
From original material by Paddy Gannon.

Editors: Sarah Armstrong, Duncan Lindsay, Andy Park and Charlotte Whiteley.
Contributor: Jason Howell

ISBN: 978 1 78294 687 8

With thanks to Dave Ryan, Glenn Rogers and Mark Edwards for the proofreading.

With thanks to Ana Pungartnik for the copyright research.

Data used to construct stopping distance diagram on page 11 from the Highway Code.
Contains public sector information licensed under the Open Government Licence v3.0.
http://www.nationalarchives.gov.uk/doc/open-government-licence/version/3/

Printed by Elanders Ltd, Newcastle upon Tyne.
Clipart from Corel®

Based on the Classic CGP style created by Richard Parsons.

Text, design, layout and original illustrations © Coordination Group Publications Ltd (CGP) 2017
All rights reserved.

Photocopying more than one section of this book is not permitted, even if you have a CLA licence.
Extra copies are available from CGP with next day delivery • 0800 1712 712 • www.cgpbooks.co.uk

Velocity and Acceleration

Speed and velocity are similar, but in physics they're not quite the same...

Speed and Velocity are Both How Fast You're Going

Speed and velocity both simply say how fast you're going, and both are measured in m/s (or km/h or mph). But there is a subtle difference between them which you need to know:

> Speed is just how fast you're going (e.g. 30 mph or 20 m/s) with no regard to the direction.
> Velocity however must also have the direction specified, e.g. 30 mph north or 20 m/s, 060°.

1) This means you can have objects travelling at a constant speed with a changing velocity. This happens when the object is changing direction whilst staying at the same speed.

2) For any object, the distance moved, (average) speed, and time taken are related by this formula:

You'd use the same formula to calculate velocity.

$$\text{Average speed} = \frac{\text{Distance moved}}{\text{Time taken}}$$

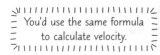

If you're not sure how to use formula triangles, have a look inside the back cover.

Example: A cat skulks 20 m in 35 s.
Find: a) its average speed, b) how long it takes to skulk 75 m.

Using the formula triangle: a) $v = s/t = 20/35 = \underline{0.57 \text{ m/s}}$ (to 2 d.p.)
b) $t = s/v = 75/0.57 = 132 \text{ s} = \underline{2 \text{ min } 12 \text{ s}}$

Acceleration is How Quickly Velocity is Changing

1) Acceleration is not the same as velocity or speed. Acceleration is how quickly the velocity is changing.

2) This change in velocity can be a CHANGE IN SPEED or a CHANGE IN DIRECTION or both. You only have to worry about the change in speed bit for calculations.

3) The unit of acceleration is m/s². Not m/s, which is velocity, but m/s².

4) There are two formulas you need to know:

The formulas for acceleration on this page only work when the acceleration is constant.

① $$\text{Acceleration} = \frac{\text{Change in Velocity}}{\text{Time taken}}$$

Here 'v' is the final velocity and 'u' is the initial velocity.

There's a slightly tricky thing with this formula — the '$(v - u)$' means working out the 'change in velocity', rather than just putting a simple value for velocity or speed in.

A negative value for acceleration means something is slowing down (decelerating).

Example: A skulking cat accelerates from 2 m/s to 6 m/s in 5.6 s. Find its acceleration.

Using the formula triangle: $a = (v - u) / t = (6 - 2) / 5.6 = 4 \div 5.6 = \underline{0.71 \text{ m/s}^2}$

② $$v^2 = u^2 + 2as$$

Here 'v' is the final velocity, 'u' is the initial velocity, and 's' is the distance travelled while accelerating.

Example: A van travelling at 23 m/s starts decelerating uniformly at 2.0 m/s² as it heads towards a built-up area 112 m away. What will its speed be when it reaches the built-up area?

1) Put the numbers in — remember a is negative because it's a deceleration.

$v^2 = u^2 + (2 \times a \times s)$
$= 23^2 + (2 \times -2.0 \times 112) = 81$

2) Finally, square root the whole thing.

$v = \sqrt{81} = \underline{9 \text{ m/s}}$

Don't speed through this page — learn it properly...

You might not be told what equation to use in the exam, so make sure you can spot when to use each equation.

Q1 a) A sprinter runs 200 m in 25 s. Calculate his average speed. [1 mark]
b) As he crosses the line, the sprinter is travelling at the speed in part a).
It then takes him 2 seconds to come to a complete stop. Calculate his acceleration. [2 marks]

Distance-Time and Velocity-Time Graphs

Make sure you learn all these details properly. Make sure you can <u>distinguish</u> between the two, too.

Distance-Time Graphs Tell You How Far Something has Travelled

The different parts of a distance-time graph describe the <u>motion</u> of an object:

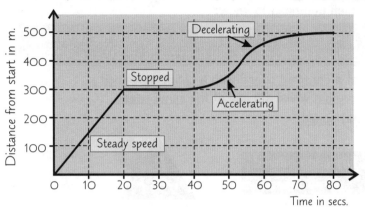

- The <u>gradient</u> (slope) at any point gives the <u>speed</u> of the object.
- <u>Flat</u> sections are where it's <u>stopped</u>.
- A <u>steeper</u> graph means it's going <u>faster</u>.
- <u>Curves</u> represent <u>acceleration</u>.
- A <u>curve getting steeper</u> means it's <u>speeding up</u> (increasing gradient).
- A <u>levelling off curve</u> means it's <u>slowing down</u> (decreasing gradient).

In the above graph, the <u>speed</u> of the <u>first</u> section (between 0 and 20 s) is:

$$\text{Speed} = \text{gradient} = \frac{\text{vertical}}{\text{horizontal}} = \frac{300}{20} = \underline{15 \text{ m/s}}$$

Don't forget that you have to use the scales of the axes to work out the gradient. Don't measure in cm!

- You can also calculate the <u>average speed</u> of an object over a period of time by <u>dividing</u> the <u>total distance</u> travelled by the <u>time</u> it takes to travel that distance. For example, the <u>average speed</u> over the whole journey is 500 ÷ 80 = <u>6.25 m/s</u>

Velocity-Time Graphs can have a Positive or Negative Gradient

How an object's <u>velocity</u> changes over time can be plotted on a <u>velocity-time</u> graph.

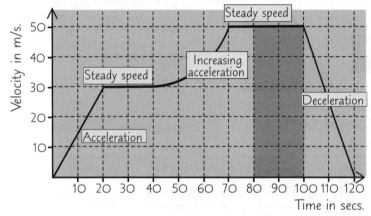

- <u>Gradient = acceleration</u>.
- <u>Flat</u> sections represent <u>steady</u> speed.
- The <u>steeper</u> the graph, the <u>greater</u> the acceleration or deceleration.
- <u>Uphill</u> sections (/) are <u>acceleration</u>.
- <u>Downhill</u> sections (\) are <u>deceleration</u>.
- The <u>area</u> under any part of the graph is equal to the <u>distance</u> travelled in that <u>time</u> interval.
- A <u>curve</u> means <u>changing acceleration</u>.

1) The <u>acceleration</u> represented by the <u>first section</u> of the graph is:

$$\text{Acceleration} = \text{gradient} = \frac{\text{vertical}}{\text{horizontal}} = \frac{30}{20} = \underline{1.5 \text{ m/s}^2}$$

2) The <u>speed</u> at any point is simply found by <u>reading the value</u> off the <u>velocity axis</u>.

3) The <u>distance travelled</u> in any time interval is equal to the <u>area</u> under the graph.

The distance travelled between $t = 80$ s and $t = 100$ s is equal to the <u>shaded area</u>, which is equal to 50 m/s × 20 s = <u>1000 m</u>

Some maths — oh good...

For practice, try sketching distance-time graphs for different scenarios. Like walking home or running from a bear.

Q1   Sketch a distance-time graph for an object that initially accelerates, then travels at a constant speed, then decelerates to a stop.   [2 marks]

Mass, Weight and Gravity

The information on this page may come as a surprise, but it's true — mass and weight are NOT the same thing. You need to learn about gravity first, then you'll appreciate the differences...

Gravity is the Force of Attraction Between All Masses

Gravity attracts all masses, but you only notice it when one of the masses is really really big, e.g. a planet. Anything near a planet or star is attracted to it very strongly.

This has three important effects:

1) On the surface of a planet, it makes all things accelerate towards the ground (all with the same acceleration, g, which is about 10 m/s² on Earth).

2) It gives everything a weight.

3) It keeps planets, moons and satellites in their orbits. The orbit is a balance between the forward motion of the object and the force of gravity pulling it inwards (see page 74).

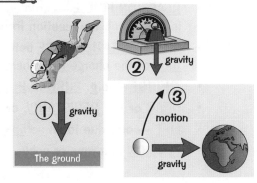

Weight and Mass are Not the Same

To understand this you must learn all these facts about mass and weight:

1) Mass is just the amount of 'stuff' in an object. For any given object this will have the same value anywhere in the universe.

2) Weight is caused by the pull of gravity. In most questions the weight of an object is just the force of gravity pulling it towards the centre of the Earth.

3) An object has the same mass whether it's on Earth or on the Moon — but its weight will be different. A 1 kg mass will weigh less on the Moon (about 1.6 N) than it does on Earth (about 10 N), simply because the force of gravity pulling on it is less.

4) Weight is a force measured in newtons. It's measured using a spring balance or newton meter. Mass is not a force. It's measured in kilograms with a mass balance (an old-fashioned pair of balancing scales).

The Very Important Formula Relating Mass, Weight and Gravity

| weight = mass × gravitational field strength | $W = m \times g$ |

1) Remember, weight and mass are not the same. Mass is in kilograms (kg), weight is in newtons (N).

2) The letter "g" represents the strength of the gravity and its value is different for different planets. On Earth $g \approx 10$ N/kg. On the Moon, where the gravity is weaker, g is only about 1.6 N/kg.

3) This formula is hideously easy to use:

> **Example:** What is the weight, in newtons, of a 5 kg mass, both on Earth and on the Moon?
>
> Use the formula $W = m \times g$.
>
> On Earth: $W = 5 \times 10 = \underline{50 \text{ N}}$ (The weight of the 5 kg mass is 50 N.)
> On the Moon: $W = 5 \times 1.6 = \underline{8 \text{ N}}$ (The weight of the 5 kg mass is 8 N.)

See what I mean. Hideously easy — as long as you've learnt what all the letters mean.

Learn about gravity now — no point in "weighting" around...

Remember that weight is a force due to gravity and that it changes depending on the strength of the gravitational field the object is in. Gravity can cause circular motion in things like moons and satellites — see page 74.

Q1   Calculate the weight in newtons of a 32 kg mass:
a) on Earth ($g \approx 10$ N/kg)
b) on the Moon ($g \approx 1.6$ N/kg)

[2 marks]

Forces and Friction

Forces are your friends — without them, you'd never get anywhere, and movement would be impossible.

There are Loads of Different Types of Force

A <u>force</u> is simply a <u>push</u> or a <u>pull</u>. There are lots of different types of force you need to know about:

- <u>GRAVITY</u> or <u>WEIGHT</u> (see previous page) — close to a planet this acts <u>straight downwards</u>.
- <u>REACTION FORCE</u> — acts <u>perpendicular</u> to a surface and away from it (so if the surface is <u>horizontal</u>, the reaction force acts <u>straight upwards</u>.)
- <u>ELECTROSTATIC FORCE</u> between two <u>charged</u> objects. The direction depends on the <u>type</u> of the charge (<u>like</u> charges <u>repel</u>, <u>opposite</u> charges <u>attract</u>) — see page 23.
- <u>THRUST</u> — e.g. <u>PUSH</u> or <u>PULL</u> due to an engine or rocket <u>speeding something up</u>.
- <u>DRAG</u> or <u>AIR RESISTANCE</u> or <u>FRICTION</u> which is <u>slowing the thing down</u>.
- <u>LIFT</u> — e.g. due to an <u>aeroplane wing</u>.
- <u>TENSION</u> in a <u>rope</u> or <u>cable</u>.

You Can Draw the Forces Acting on a Body

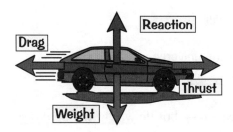

1) Chances are, there are <u>loads</u> of forces acting on you right now that you don't even know about. You don't notice them because they all <u>balance out</u>.

2) Any object with a <u>weight</u> feels a <u>reaction force</u> back from the surface it's on. Otherwise it would just keep <u>falling</u>.

3) When an object <u>moves</u> in a <u>fluid</u> (air, water etc.) it feels <u>drag</u> in the <u>opposite direction</u> to its motion.

Friction is Always There to Slow things Down

1) If an object has <u>no force</u> propelling it along, it will always <u>slow down and stop</u> because of <u>friction</u> (unless you're out in space where there's no friction). Friction is a <u>force</u> that <u>opposes motion</u>.

2) To travel at a <u>steady speed</u>, things always need a <u>driving force</u> to <u>counteract</u> the friction.

3) Friction occurs in <u>three main ways</u>:

a) Friction Between Solid Surfaces Which Are Gripping
(static friction) ⟹

b) Friction Between Solid Surfaces Which Are Sliding Past Each Other

You can <u>reduce</u> both these types of friction by putting a <u>lubricant</u> like <u>oil</u> or <u>grease</u> between the surfaces. Friction between <u>solids</u> can often cause <u>wear</u> of the two <u>surfaces</u> in contact.

c) Resistance or "drag" from fluids (liquids or gases, e.g. air)

The most important factor <u>by far</u> in <u>reducing drag in fluids</u> is keeping the shape of the object <u>streamlined</u>, like sports cars or boat hulls. Lorries and caravans have "<u>deflectors</u>" on them to make them more streamlined and reduce drag.

<u>Roof boxes</u> on cars spoil their streamlined shape and so slow them down. For a given thrust, the <u>higher</u> the <u>drag</u>, the <u>lower</u> the <u>top speed</u> of the car.

The <u>opposite extreme</u> to a sports car is a <u>parachute</u> which is about as <u>high drag</u> as you can get — which is, of course, <u>the whole idea</u>.

In a <u>fluid</u>, <u>FRICTION ALWAYS INCREASES AS THE SPEED INCREASES</u> — see page 9.

This stuff can be a little hard to swallow — you might have to force it down...

We owe a lot to forces really, quietly making the world go round.

Q1   A book is at rest on a table. Draw a diagram showing all the forces acting upon it.   [1 mark]

Investigating Motion

There's no use in knowing about <u>speed</u>, <u>velocity</u> and <u>acceleration</u> if you don't know how they can be used to describe an object's motion. Here's a simple toy car experiment you can try out yourself.

You can Investigate the Motion of a Toy Car on a Ramp

1) Set up your apparatus like in the diagram below, holding the car still just before the first light gate.

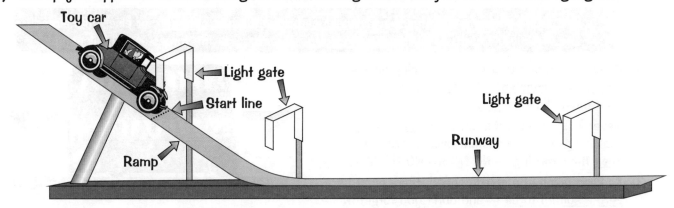

2) Mark a <u>line</u> on the ramp — this is to make sure the car starts from the <u>same point</u> each time.

3) Measure the <u>distance</u> between each light gate — you'll need this to find the car's <u>average speed</u>.

4) <u>Let go</u> of the car just before the light gate so that it starts to roll down the slope.

5) The light gates should be connected to a <u>computer</u>. When the car passes through each <u>light gate</u>, a beam of light is broken and a time is recorded by <u>data-logging software</u>.

6) <u>Repeat</u> this experiment several times and get an <u>average time</u> it takes for the car to reach each light gate.

> Using light gates means you don't get any timing errors as a result of a person reacting slowly. If you don't have light gates, you could use a stopwatch with a lap function.

7) Using these times and the distances between light gates you can find the <u>average speed</u> of the car on the ramp and the average speed of the car on the runway — just divide the <u>distance</u> <u>between the light gates</u> by the average <u>time taken</u> for the car to travel between gates (page 1).

You Could Play Around with the Experimental Set-up

You could change <u>different things</u> in this <u>experiment</u> to investigate <u>other</u> <u>factors</u> that might affect the car's motion. Just make sure that if you do change something, every other part of the experiment stays <u>the same</u>.

1) You could try seeing if the <u>mass</u> of the car affects its average speed — just load weights onto it (but make sure you don't overload it so that the wheel axles grind).

2) To see how <u>friction</u> affects the motion of the car you could try placing different materials on the ramp. If you do this, make sure they're laid <u>flat</u> and they don't change the <u>angle</u> of the ramp in any way.

3) You could investigate the <u>acceleration</u> of the car due to gravity by starting it off higher up the ramp and seeing how this affects its <u>average speed</u> between the gates.

4) You could change the <u>angle</u> of the ramp to see how that affects the car's speed down the slope.

5) You could even try it with <u>different cars</u> — see how the size, shape and weight of the car affects how fast it goes down the ramp.

> You'd expect the more streamlined ones to go quicker — see page 4.

If you want to investigate motion you'll need to invest in gates...

Make sure you know multiple methods for measuring the speed of an object.

Q1   Why is it better to use a light gate instead of a stopwatch to measure short time intervals?   [1 mark]

The Three Laws of Motion

Around about the time of the Great Plague in the 1660s, a chap called Isaac Newton worked out the Three Laws of Motion. At first they might seem kind of obscure or irrelevant, but to be perfectly blunt, if you can't understand these three simple laws then you'll never understand forces and motion:

First Law — Balanced Forces Mean No Change in Velocity

> So long as the forces on an object are all balanced, then it'll just stay still, or else if it's already moving it'll just carry on at the same velocity — so long as the forces are all balanced.

1) When a train or car or bus or anything else is moving at a constant velocity then the forces on it must all be balanced.

2) Never let yourself entertain the ridiculous idea that things need a constant overall force to keep them moving — NO NO NO NO NO NO!

3) To keep going at a steady speed, there must be zero resultant force — and don't you forget it.

Second Law — A Resultant Force Means Acceleration

> If there is an unbalanced force, then the object will accelerate in that direction.

1) The overall unbalanced force is often called the resultant force (see page 7).

2) An unbalanced (or resultant) force will always produce acceleration (or deceleration).

3) This "acceleration" can take five different forms:
   - Starting
   - stopping
   - speeding up
   - slowing down
   - changing direction.

4) On a force diagram, the arrows will be unequal:

> - Don't ever say: "If something's moving there must be an overall resultant force acting on it".
> - Not so. If there's an overall force it will always accelerate.
> - You get steady speed from balanced forces.
>   I wonder how many times I need to say that same thing before you remember it?

Resultant Force = Mass × Acceleration

The three points below are probably pretty obvious:

1) The bigger the force, the greater the acceleration or deceleration.

2) The bigger the mass, the smaller the acceleration.

3) To get a big mass to accelerate as fast as a small mass it needs a bigger force. Just think about pushing heavy trolleys and it should all make sense.

In a nutshell, any resultant force will produce acceleration, and this is the formula for it:

Force = mass × acceleration
$F = ma$

m = mass
a = acceleration
F is always the resultant force

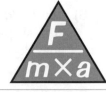

The fun's not over — there's one more law of motion still to come...

You've only seen two laws of motion on this page, so the fun continues on the next page. But try this question first...

Q1   A boat is travelling at a constant velocity. What is the resultant force acting on the boat?   [1 mark]

The Three Laws of Motion

You can use Newton's second law to find an object's <u>acceleration</u>. All you need to know is the object's <u>mass</u> and the <u>resultant force</u> acting on it. You might have to rearrange the equation first though...

Resultant Force is Real Important — Especially for "F = ma"

1) The notion of <u>resultant force</u> is a really important one for you to get your head round. It's not especially tricky — it's just that it seems to get kind of <u>ignored</u>.

2) In most <u>real</u> situations there are at least <u>two forces</u> acting on an object along any direction. The <u>overall</u> effect of these forces will decide the <u>motion</u> of the object — whether it will <u>accelerate</u>, <u>decelerate</u> or stay at a <u>steady speed</u>.

3) If the forces act along the same line, the "<u>overall effect</u>" is found by just <u>adding or subtracting</u> them (see next page). The overall force you get is called the <u>resultant force</u>. When you use the <u>formula</u> "<u>F = ma</u>", *F* must always be the <u>resultant force</u>.

Example:	A car of mass of 1750 kg has an engine which provides a resultant driving force of 5200 N. Find the car's acceleration.

* First draw a force diagram for the car — this will make the situation easier to understand:
* Apply "*F = ma*" using the formula triangle:

$a = F/m$
$= 5200 \div 1750$
$= \underline{3.0 \text{ m/s}^2}$

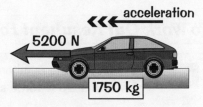

acceleration
5200 N
1750 kg

The Third Law — Reaction Forces

> If object A <u>exerts a force</u> on object B then object B exerts <u>an equal and opposite force</u> on object A.

This is Newton's third law of motion.

1) That means if you <u>push</u> something, say a shopping trolley, the trolley will <u>push back</u> against you, <u>just as hard</u>.

2) And as soon as you <u>stop</u> pushing, <u>so does the trolley</u>. Kinda clever really.

3) So far so good. The slightly tricky thing to get your head round is this — if the forces are always equal, <u>how does anything ever go anywhere</u>? The important thing to remember is that the two forces are acting on <u>different objects</u>. Think about a pair of ice skaters:

Skater A   Skater B

mass = 55 kg   mass = 65 kg

* When skater A pushes on skater B (the '<u>action</u>' force), she feels an equal and opposite force from skater B's hand (the '<u>reaction</u>' force).
* Both skaters feel the <u>same sized force</u>, in <u>opposite directions</u>, and so accelerate away from each other.
* Skater A will be <u>accelerated</u> more than skater B, though, because she has a <u>smaller mass</u> — remember <u>F = ma</u>.

4) It's the same sort of thing when you go <u>swimming</u>. You <u>push</u> back against the <u>water</u> with your arms and legs, and the water pushes you forwards with an <u>equal-sized force</u> in the <u>opposite direction</u>.

Paper 2

I have a reaction to forces — they bring me out in a rash...

Newton's 3rd law really trips people up, so make sure you understand exactly what objects the forces are acting on and how that results in movement (or lack of it). Then have a crack at this question to practise what you know.

Q1   A full shopping trolley and an empty one are moving at the same speed. Explain why it is easier to stop the empty trolley than the full trolley over the same amount of time.

[1 mark]

Combining Forces

When you're talking about the forces acting on an object, it's not enough to just talk about the <u>size</u> of each force. You need to know their <u>direction</u> too so you know which way the object will accelerate.

Vectors Have Size and Direction — Scalar Quantities Only Have Size

1) When there are <u>multiple forces</u> acting on an object, it's often useful to know the <u>resultant force</u> acting on the object (see page 7). To do this you need to know the <u>size</u> of all the <u>different forces</u> acting on the object and their <u>direction</u>.

2) Force is a <u>vector quantity</u> — vector quantities have a <u>size</u> and a <u>direction</u>.

3) Lots of <u>physical quantities</u> are vector quantities:

> <u>Vector quantities</u>: force, velocity, acceleration, momentum, etc.

Vector quantities are usually represented by arrows.

4) Some physical quantities <u>only</u> have size and <u>no direction</u>. These are called <u>scalar quantities</u>:

> <u>Scalar quantities</u>: mass, temperature, time, length, etc.

To Work Out Resultant Force You Need To Combine Vectors

Example: What's the resultant force of a 220 N force north, a 180 N force south and a 90 N force south?

Start by choosing a direction as the positive — let's say north. This means you <u>add</u> any forces in the north direction and <u>subtract</u> any forces in the south direction.

Resultant force = 220 – 180 – 90 = –50 N, so <u>50 N south</u>.

Example:

a) The jets on the plane are producing a thrust of 22 000 N east, and the friction from the air is 8000 N west at this speed. What is the resultant force acting on the plane?

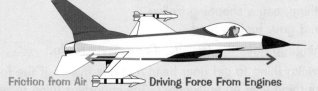

Friction from Air ← → Driving Force From Engines

Draw the vectors <u>end to end</u>:

Engine thrust 22 000 N east + Friction 8000 N west = Resultant Force 14 000 N east

b) Find the acceleration of the plane in part a) if it has a mass of 10 000 kg.

Rearrange $F = ma$ (page 6) using the formula triangle to give:

$a = F/m = 14\ 000 \div 10\ 000 = \underline{1.4\ m/s^2}$

What's a vector's favourite band? One Direction...

You use the same trick to combine any vectors — velocity vectors, momentum vectors, acceleration vectors, and so on (but don't mix different kinds of vectors — you can't add a velocity vector to an acceleration, for example). Just draw the vectors end to end and, with a bit of simple maths, you can find the overall (resultant) vector.

Q1 A 2 kg mass is on the end of a stretched spring. Its weight is a force of approximately 20 N and acts vertically downwards. The spring exerts a force on the mass of 24 N directed vertically upwards.
a) Find the resultant force acting on the mass. [1 mark]
b) Calculate the acceleration of the mass. [2 marks]

Terminal Velocity

Okay... so we all know that gravity is responsible for accelerating skydivers towards the ground when they jump out of a plane. But have you ever wondered why they don't keep on accelerating and go faster and faster and faster... maybe not... but you're about to find out anyway.

Moving Objects Can Reach a Terminal Velocity

This whole terminal velocity thing is explained by Newton's laws of motion (see page 6).

Frictional forces increase with speed — but only up to a certain point.

1) When an object first starts to fall, it has much more force accelerating it than resistance slowing it down.

2) As its velocity increases, the resistance builds up.

It's a bit like when you (very carefully) put your hand out of the window of a car as it moves along. At low speeds, you hardly notice the air pushing against your hand. But as the car goes faster, the air pushes your hand backwards much harder.

3) This resistance force gradually reduces the acceleration until eventually the resistance force is equal to the accelerating force. At this point, the object won't be able to accelerate any more. It will have reached its maximum velocity or terminal velocity.

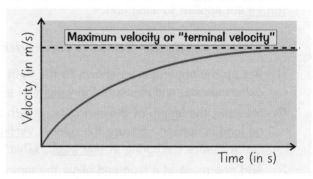

The Terminal Velocity of Falling Objects Depends on Their Shape and Area

1) The accelerating force acting on all falling objects is gravity and it would make them all accelerate at the same rate, if it wasn't for air resistance.

2) To prove this, on the Moon, where there's no air, hamsters and feathers dropped simultaneously will hit the ground together.

3) However, on Earth, air resistance causes things to fall at different speeds, and the terminal velocity of any object is determined by its drag compared to its weight. The drag depends on its shape and area.

The most important example is the human skydiver.

1) Without his parachute open he has quite a small area and a force equal to his weight pulling him down.

2) He reaches a terminal velocity of about 120 mph.

3) But with the parachute open, there's much more air resistance (at any given speed) and still only the same force pulling him down.

4) This means his terminal velocity comes right down to about 15 mph, which is a safe speed to hit the ground at.

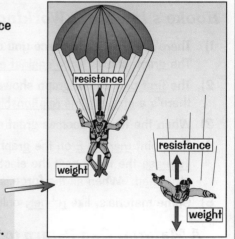

- In both cases, once the skydiver has reached terminal velocity, resistance = weight.
- The difference is the speed at which that happens.

My terminal velocity is very slow — I always get distracted by airport shops...

Just remember — the terminal velocity of an object is related to its weight and drag. Objects with a smaller weight and larger surface area have a smaller terminal velocity and so take longer to fall long distances.

Q1   Explain why an object falling through the air will eventually stop accelerating.   [2 marks]

Q2   Explain why a skydiver falls more slowly after they've opened their parachute.   [2 marks]

Hooke's Law

Applying a force to an object can cause it to change shape temporarily... or even permanently.

Hooke's Law Says that Extension is Proportional to Force

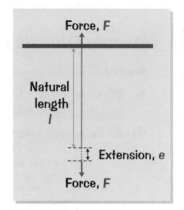

1) The length of an <u>unstretched</u> metal wire is called its <u>natural length</u>, *l*.

2) If a metal <u>wire</u> (see right) is supported at the top and then a <u>weight</u> attached to the bottom, it <u>stretches</u>. The weight pulls down with force *F*, producing an equal and opposite force at the support.

3) This will also happen to <u>helical springs</u> and any object that will stretch without immediately snapping or deforming.

4) Robert Hooke discovered in 1676 that the <u>extension</u> of a stretched wire is <u>proportional</u> to the <u>load</u>, or <u>force</u>. This relationship is now called Hooke's law.

5) A metal spring (or other object) will also obey Hooke's law if a pair of <u>opposite</u> <u>forces</u> are applied to each end.

You Can Investigate Hooke's Law with a Spring   PRACTICAL

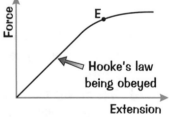

1) Set up the apparatus as shown to the right. Make sure you have plenty of extra masses, and measure the <u>weight</u> of each (with a balance).

2) Measure the <u>length</u> of the spring (e.g. with an <u>accurate</u> mm ruler) when <u>no load</u> is applied. Ensure the ruler is <u>vertical</u> (e.g. with a set square) and measure the spring at <u>eye level</u>. (This is the spring's <u>natural length</u>.)

3) Add one mass at a time and allow the spring to come to <u>rest</u>, then measure the new <u>length</u> of the spring. The <u>extension</u> is the change in length from the original length. Adding a marker to the top and bottom of the spring might make measuring lengths easier. <u>Repeat</u> this process until you have enough measurements (no fewer than 6).

4) Once you're done, <u>repeat</u> the experiment and calculate an <u>average</u> value for the length of the spring for each applied weight.

5) Plot your results on a <u>graph</u> — show <u>force</u> (i.e. the total <u>weight</u>) on the <u>vertical axis</u> and the <u>total extension</u> on the <u>horizontal axis</u>. You should find that the same increase in the <u>weight</u> on the end of the spring always leads to the same increase in <u>extension</u> — this is Hooke's law in action.

6) <u>Repeat</u> the experiment using a <u>metal wire</u> or a <u>rubber band</u> instead of the spring.

Hooke's law Stops Working when the Force is Great Enough

1) There's a <u>limit</u> to the force you can apply for Hooke's law to stay true. The graph shows <u>force against extension</u> for a typical <u>metal wire</u>.

2) The <u>first part</u> of the graph shows <u>Hooke's law</u> being <u>obeyed</u> — there's a <u>straight-line relationship</u> between force and extension.

3) When the force becomes great enough, the graph starts to <u>curve</u>.

4) The point <u>marked E</u> on the graph is called the <u>elastic limit</u>. If you <u>increase</u> the force <u>past</u> the elastic limit, the material will be <u>permanently stretched</u>. When all the force is removed, the material will be <u>longer</u> than at the start.

5) Some materials, like <u>rubber</u>, only obey Hooke's law for really <u>small extensions</u>.

A Material Can Return to its Original Shape After an Elastic Deformation

1) If a material returns to its <u>original shape</u> once the forces are removed, it displays <u>elastic behaviour</u>.

2) Metals display elastic behaviour as long as <u>Hooke's law</u> is obeyed.

Sod's law — if you don't learn it, it'll be in the exam...

Okay, so this isn't the most riveting stuff in the world — but at least it's fairly simple.

Q1   What does a force-extension graph demonstrating Hooke's law look like?   [2 marks]

Stopping Distances

Looking at things simply — if you <u>need to stop</u> in a <u>given distance</u>... then the <u>faster</u> you're going, the <u>bigger braking force</u> you'll need. But in real life there are loads of <u>other factors</u> too...

Many Factors *Affect* Your Total Stopping Distance

1) The stopping distance of a car is the distance covered in the time between the driver <u>first spotting</u> a hazard and the car coming to a <u>complete stop</u>. They're pretty keen on this for exam questions, so make sure you <u>learn it properly</u>.

2) The distance it takes to stop a car is divided into the <u>thinking distance</u> and the <u>braking distance</u>.

Stopping Distance = Thinking Distance + Braking Distance

1) Thinking Distance

"The distance the car travels in the time between the driver noticing the hazard and applying the brakes."

It's affected by <u>two main factors</u>:

a) How fast you're going — obviously. Whatever your reaction time, the <u>faster</u> you're going, the <u>further</u> you'll go.

b) Your reaction time — This is affected by things like <u>tiredness</u>, <u>drugs</u>, <u>alcohol</u> and <u>old age</u>. <u>Inexperience</u> can also affect your <u>reaction time</u>.

The figures below for typical stopping distances are from the Highway Code. It's frightening to see just how far it takes to stop when you're going at 70 mph.

2) Braking Distance

"The distance the car travels during its deceleration whilst the brakes are being applied."

It's affected by <u>four main factors</u>:

a) How fast you're going — The <u>faster</u> you're going the <u>further</u> it takes to stop.

b) The mass of the vehicle — with the <u>same</u> brakes, the <u>larger the mass</u> of a vehicle, the <u>longer it takes to stop</u>. A car won't stop as quickly when it's full of people and luggage and towing a caravan.

c) How good your brakes are — all brakes must be checked and maintained <u>regularly</u>. Worn or faulty brakes will let you down <u>catastrophically</u> just when you need them the <u>most</u>, i.e. in an <u>emergency</u>.

d) How good the grip is — this depends on <u>three things</u>:
   1) <u>road surface</u>,
   2) <u>weather</u> conditions,
   3) <u>tyres</u>.

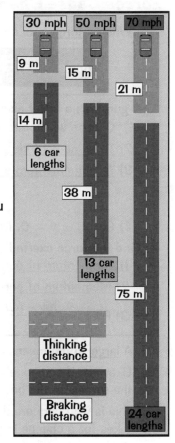

To avoid an accident, drivers need to leave <u>enough space</u> between their car and the one in front so that if they have to stop suddenly they can do so <u>safely</u>. 'Enough space' means the <u>stopping distance</u> for whatever speed they're going at. <u>Speed limits</u> are important because <u>speed</u> affects <u>stopping distance</u> so much.

Bad visibility can also be a major factor in accidents — lashing rain, thick fog, bright oncoming lights, etc. might mean that a driver doesn't notice a hazard until they're quite close to it — so they have a much shorter distance available to stop in.

Stop right there — and learn this page...

Leaves, diesel spills and muck on t'road are serious hazards because they're unexpected. Wet or icy roads are always much more slippy than dry roads, but often you only discover this when you try to brake.

Q1 Explain two factors that affect how quickly a vehicle can stop after the driver has noticed a hazard. [4 marks]

Momentum and Collisions

A <u>large</u> rugby player running very <u>fast</u> will be harder to stop than a <u>scrawny</u> one <u>jogging</u> — that's momentum.

Momentum = Mass × Velocity

1) The <u>greater</u> the <u>mass</u> of an object and the <u>greater</u> its <u>velocity</u>, the <u>more momentum</u> the object has.

2) Momentum is a <u>vector</u> quantity (page 8) — it has size <u>and</u> direction (like <u>velocity</u>, but not speed).

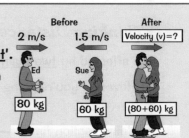

p is the symbol for momentum.

Momentum (kg m/s) = Mass (kg) × Velocity (m/s)

Momentum Before = Momentum After

<u>Momentum is conserved</u> when no external forces act — total momentum <u>after</u> is the <u>same</u> as it was <u>before</u>.

Two skaters approach each other, collide and move off together as shown. At what velocity do they move after the collision?

1) Choose which direction is <u>positive</u> — I'll say 'positive' means '<u>to the right</u>'.

2) <u>Total momentum before</u> collision = Ed's momentum + Sue's momentum
= {80 × 2} + {60 × (−1.5)}
= <u>70 kg m/s</u>

3) <u>Total momentum after</u> collision = momentum of Ed and Sue together
= <u>140 × v</u>

4) So 140v = 70, i.e. <u>v = 0.5 m/s to the right</u>

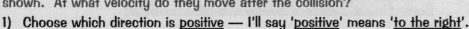

Before | After
2 m/s | 1.5 m/s | Velocity (v) = ?
Ed | Sue
80 kg | 60 kg | (80+60) kg

Forces Cause Changes in Momentum

1) When a <u>force</u> acts on an object, it causes a <u>change</u> in momentum.

$$\text{force (N)} = \frac{\text{change in momentum (kg m/s)}}{\text{time (s)}}$$ or $$F = \frac{(mv - mu)}{t}$$

A gun fires a bullet as shown. At what speed does the gun move backwards?

1) Choose which direction is <u>positive</u> — I'll use '<u>to the right</u>' as '<u>positive</u>'.

2) <u>Total momentum before</u> firing = <u>0 kg m/s</u>

3) <u>Total momentum after</u> firing = bullet's momentum + gun's momentum
= (0.01 × 150) + (1 × v)
= <u>1.5 + v</u>

4) So 1.5 + v = 0, i.e. v = −1.5 m/s. So the gun moves backwards at <u>1.5 m/s</u>.

Velocity of gun (v) = ?
Velocity of bullet = 150 m/s
mass of bullet = 0.01 kg
mass of gun = 1 kg
After firing

This is the gun's recoil.

Find the force exerted on the gun if it is accelerated for 0.1 seconds.

1) <u>Momentum of gun before</u> firing = mu = 1 × 0 = <u>0 kg m/s</u>

2) <u>Momentum of gun after</u> firing = mv = 1 × −1.5 = <u>−1.5 kg m/s</u>

3) Force = $\dfrac{mv - mu}{t} = \dfrac{-1.5 - 0}{0.1} = \underline{-15 \text{ N}}$

By Newton's Third Law, this means the force on the bullet must be 15 N in the opposite direction.

2) A <u>larger</u> force means a <u>faster</u> change of momentum (and so a greater <u>acceleration</u> — see page 6).

3) Likewise, if someone's momentum changes <u>very quickly</u> (like in a <u>car crash</u>), the <u>forces</u> on the body will be very <u>large</u>, and more likely to cause <u>injury</u>.

4) This is why cars are designed to slow people down over a <u>longer time</u> when they crash — the longer it takes for a change in <u>momentum</u>, the <u>smaller</u> the <u>force</u> (and the <u>less severe</u> the injuries are likely to be).

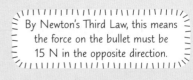

<u>CRUMPLE ZONES</u> crumple on impact, <u>increasing the time</u> taken for the car to stop.

<u>SEAT BELTS</u> stretch slightly, <u>increasing the time</u> taken for the wearer to stop. This <u>reduces the forces</u> acting on the chest.

<u>AIR BAGS</u> also slow you down more <u>gradually</u>.

Learn this stuff — it'll only take a moment... um...

Momentum is a pretty fundamental bit of physics — learn it well. Then have a go at this question.

[P2] Q1   Calculate the force needed to accelerate a 58 g tennis ball from rest to 34 m/s in 11.6 ms.   [3 marks] [P2]

Paper 2

Paper 2

Turning Effects and Centre of Gravity

Forces that cause turning effects — e.g. from good ol' spanners and levers. Not very difficult... not very exciting either. Expect to be royally sick of pivots and centre of gravity by the time you've finished these pages.

A Moment is the Turning Effect of a Force

MOMENT (Nm) = FORCE (N) × perpendicular DISTANCE (m) between line of action and pivot

1) The force on the spanner causes a turning effect or moment on the nut. A larger force would mean a larger moment.

2) Using a longer spanner, the same force can exert a larger moment because the distance from the pivot is greater.

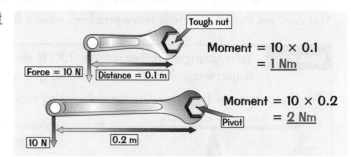

Moment = 10 × 0.1 = 1 Nm

Moment = 10 × 0.2 = 2 Nm

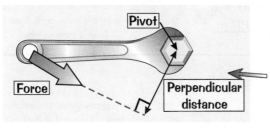

3) To get the maximum moment (or turning effect) you need to push at right angles (perpendicular) to the spanner.

4) Pushing at any other angle means a smaller moment because the perpendicular distance between the line of action and the pivot is smaller.

The Centre of Gravity Hangs Directly Below the Point of Suspension

1) You can think of the centre of gravity of an object as the point through which the weight of a body acts.

2) A freely suspended object will swing until its centre of gravity is vertically below the point of suspension.

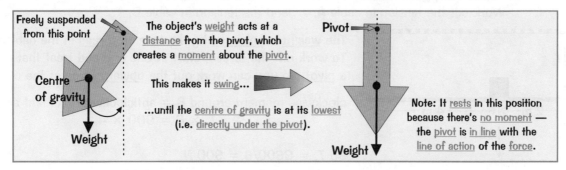

The object's weight acts at a distance from the pivot, which creates a moment about the pivot.

This makes it swing...

...until the centre of gravity is at its lowest (i.e. directly under the pivot).

Note: It rests in this position because there's no moment — the pivot is in line with the line of action of the force.

3) This means you can find the centre of gravity of any flat shape like this:

1) Suspend the shape and a plumb line from the same point, and wait until they stop moving.

2) Draw a line along the plumb line.

3) Do the same thing again, but suspend the shape from a different pivot point.

4) The centre of gravity is where your two lines cross.

Picture of snowman.

4) But you don't need to go to all that trouble for simple shapes. You can quickly guess where the centre of gravity is by looking for lines of symmetry.

Okay — this one's trickier.

Take a moment to find your centre...

Think of the extra force you need to open a door by pushing it near the hinge compared to at the handle — the distance from pivot is less, so you need more force to get the same moment. Best way to understand it is to get loads of practice.

Q1 A 10 N force is applied at right angles to a door, 85 cm from its hinges. Find the moment created. [1 mark]

Principle of Moments

Once you can calculate moments, you can work out if a <u>seesaw is balanced</u>. Useful thing, Physics.

A Question of Balance — Are the Moments Equal?

The <u>principle of moments</u> says:

> If an object is balanced then:
> Total <u>Anticlockwise</u> Moments = Total <u>Clockwise</u> Moments

You can use this idea to help solve problems where forces are acting on a <u>balanced object</u>.

Example: Your younger brother weighs 300 N and sits 2 m from the pivot of a seesaw. If you weigh 700 N, where should you sit to balance the seesaw?

For the seesaw to <u>balance</u>: Total <u>anticlockwise</u> moments = total <u>clockwise</u> moments

anticlockwise moment = clockwise moment
$$300 \times 2 = 700 \times y$$
$$y = \underline{0.86 \text{ m}}$$

Ignore the weight of the seesaw — its centre of mass is on the pivot, so it doesn't have a turning effect.

Forces are Not Always Equal Across All Supports

"Light" means you can ignore the weight in your calculations. In general, if they don't tell you the weight, you can ignore it.

1) If a <u>light rod</u> is being supported at <u>both ends</u>, the <u>upwards force</u> provided by each support <u>won't</u> always be the <u>same</u>.

2) If a <u>heavy object</u> is placed on the rod, the support <u>closest</u> to the object will provide a <u>larger force</u>.

Example: A 6 m long light rod is suspended by two cables (A and B) at its ends. A 900 N weight is placed 4 m from one end, as shown below. Work out the tension in cable A, T_A, and the tension in cable B, T_B.

The <u>weight</u> is <u>balanced</u> by the tension <u>forces</u> in the cables. To work out the forces, start at one end and treat that end as a <u>pivot</u>, so you can work out the <u>upward force</u> at the other end:

clockwise moment around B = anticlockwise moment around B
$$T_A \times 6 = 900 \times 4$$

So $T_A = 3600/6 = \underline{600 \text{ N}}$

Then you can work out the force in B as we know the vertical forces balance:

$$900 \text{ N} = T_A + T_B$$
So $T_B = 900 - T_A = 900 - 600 = \underline{300 \text{ N}}$

And if the Moments are Not Equal...

> If the Total <u>Anticlockwise</u> Moments <u>do not equal</u> the Total <u>Clockwise</u> Moments, there will be a <u>Resultant Moment</u>

...so the object will <u>turn</u>.

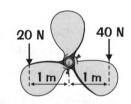

clockwise moments = $40 \times 1 = 40$ Nm
anticlockwise moments = $20 \times 1 = 20$ Nm
so the propellor will turn <u>clockwise</u>.

Balanced moments — nope, not had one of those for a while...

Any time you've got equal clockwise and anticlockwise moments, you've got equilibrium, and your thing-on-a-pivot will stay still. Remember that and you won't go far wrong (as long as you calculate moments properly).

Q1 How far from the pivot should a 27 N anticlockwise force be applied to balance a 108 Nm clockwise moment? [2 marks]

Revision Questions for Section 1

Well, that nearly wraps up forces and motion... but you're not quite done yet.

- Try these questions and <u>tick off each one</u> when you <u>get it right</u>.
- When you've done <u>all the questions</u> for a topic and are <u>completely happy</u> with it, tick off the topic.

<u>Speed, Distance and Time (p.1-2)</u> ☑

1) What's the relationship between the average speed, distance moved and time for a moving object?

2) How long would a robot take to reach 2.7 m/s from rest if it had an acceleration of 0.5 m/s²?

3) What does a straight, horizontal line show on a distance-time graph?

4) What does a straight, horizontal line show on a velocity-time graph?

5) How can you find the acceleration of an object from its velocity-time graph?

6) How could you find the distance travelled by an object from its velocity-time graph?

<u>Forces and Newton's Laws of Motion (p.3-9)</u> ☑

7) What's the force that acts between all masses called?

8) What's the difference between mass and weight?

9) The value of g on the moon is 1.6 N/kg. How much would a mass of 60 kg weigh on the Moon?

10) In what direction does friction always act, and how does friction change with the speed of an object?

11) Describe a simple experiment you could carry out to investigate the motion of a toy car.

12) What will happen to the velocity of a moving object if there is an unbalanced force on it?

13) What's the relationship between force, mass and acceleration?

14) A 25 kg rock is hurled with a force of 25 000 N. What will its acceleration be?

15) What is Newton's third law of motion?

16) What's the difference between a vector quantity and a scalar quantity? Which of these is force?

17) What's the resultant force on a train with a driving force of 19 000 N and a drag of 13 500 N?

18) Why does a falling object reach a terminal velocity?

<u>Hooke's Law, Stopping Distances and Momentum (p.10-12)</u> ☑

19) Describe a simple experiment you could use to investigate Hooke's law using a metal wire.

20) What does elastic behaviour mean?

21) State two factors that could affect how far a vehicle travels between the driver noticing a hazard and starting to brake.

22) What's the relationship between momentum, mass and velocity?

23) What's the mass of a car that has a momentum of 14 700 kg m/s when moving at 15 m/s?

24) A 2.5 kg kitten hurtles into a stationary 3.7 kg puppy at 5 m/s and sticks. Find their speed after the collision.

25) A car's brakes apply a force of 230 N for 10 seconds. Find its change in momentum.

26) How do crumple zones in cars reduce the risk of injury to the passengers in a crash?

<u>Turning Forces and Moments (p.13-14)</u> ☑

27) Find the moment produced by a 5 N force acting at a perpendicular distance of 1.3 m from a pivot.

28) What name is given to the point through which all of an object's weight acts?

29) A light rod is supported by two bricks, one at each end of the rod. Which brick feels more force when a mass is placed on one end?

Circuits — The Basics

Electricity's great. But not if the words don't mean anything to you. Hey, I know — learn them now!

The Properties of a Circuit

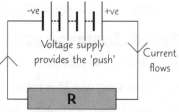

Voltage supply provides the 'push'

-ve   +ve

Current flows

R

RESISTANCE - opposes the flow

1) <u>Current</u> is the rate of <u>flow</u> of <u>charge</u> round the circuit.
   <u>Electrons</u> usually carry the charge — they're <u>negatively charged</u> particles.
   Current will <u>only flow</u> through a component if there is a <u>voltage</u> across
   that component.   Unit: ampere (amp for short), A.

2) <u>Voltage</u> is what drives the current round the circuit. Kind of like
   "<u>electrical pressure</u>". You may also see it called <u>potential difference</u>
   (or p.d.).   Unit: volt, V.

3) <u>Resistance</u> is anything in the circuit which <u>slows the flow down</u>. If you add <u>more components</u> to the
   circuit (one after the other) there will be a <u>higher overall resistance</u>.   Unit: ohm, Ω.

4) There's a <u>balance</u>. The <u>voltage</u> is trying to <u>push</u> the current round the circuit, and the <u>resistance</u> is
   <u>opposing</u> it — the <u>relative sizes</u> of the voltage and resistance decide <u>how big</u> the current will be:

> If you <u>increase the voltage</u> — then <u>more current</u> will flow.
> If you <u>increase the resistance</u> — then <u>less current</u> will flow
> (or <u>more voltage</u> will be needed to keep the <u>same current</u> flowing).

The Standard Test Circuit

This is without doubt the most totally bog-standard circuit the world has ever known. So know it.

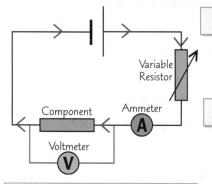

Variable Resistor

Component

Ammeter

A

Voltmeter

V

The Ammeter

1) Measures the <u>current</u> (in <u>amps</u>) flowing through the component.

2) Must be placed <u>in series</u> (see page 19) anywhere in the
   <u>main circuit</u>, but <u>never</u> in parallel like the voltmeter.

The Voltmeter

1) Measures the <u>voltage</u> (in <u>volts</u>) across the component.

2) Must be placed <u>in parallel</u> (see page 19) around the <u>component</u> under
   test — <u>NOT</u> around the variable resistor or the battery!

Five Important Points

1) This <u>very basic</u> circuit is used for testing <u>components</u>, and for getting <u>I-V graphs</u> for them.

2) The <u>component</u>, the <u>ammeter</u> and the <u>variable resistor</u> are all in <u>series</u>, which means they can be
   put in <u>any order</u> in the main circuit. The <u>voltmeter</u>, on the other hand, can only be placed <u>in parallel</u>
   around the <u>component under test</u>, as shown. Anywhere else is a definite <u>no-no</u>.

3) As you <u>vary</u> the <u>variable resistor</u> it alters the <u>current</u> flowing through the circuit.

4) This allows you to take several <u>pairs of readings</u> from the <u>ammeter</u> and <u>voltmeter</u>.

5) You can then <u>plot</u> these values for <u>current</u> and <u>voltage</u> on a <u>I-V graph</u> (see next page).

Mains Supply is a.c., Battery Supply is d.c.

1) The UK mains electricity supply is approximately <u>230 volts</u>.

2) It is an <u>a.c. supply</u> (alternating current), which means the current is <u>constantly</u> changing direction.

3) By contrast, cells and batteries supply <u>direct current</u> (d.c.). This just means that the current keeps
   flowing in the <u>same direction</u>.

The standard test circuit — it's like an obstacle course for electricity...

Electrons in circuits actually move from –ve to +ve, but it's conventional to draw current as though it's flowing from
+ve to –ve. It's what early physicists thought (before they found out about the electrons), and it's stuck.

Q1   Draw the standard test circuit.   [2 marks]

Resistance and $V = I \times R$

The <u>voltage</u> across and <u>current</u> through a component are linked by <u>resistance</u>
— if you plot them against each other, you can see how the resistance <u>changes</u>.

There's a Formula Linking V and I

You need to <u>know</u> this formula and be able to use and <u>rearrange</u> it:

> Voltage = Current × Resistance

> **Example:** A 4 Ω resistor in a circuit has a voltage of 6 V across it.
> What is the current through the resistor?
>
> Use the formula $V = I \times R$. We need to find I,
> so the version we need is $I = V/R$.
> So $I = 6/4 = \underline{1.5\ A}$

You can use this formula to work out the resistance for a pair of values
(V, I) from an <u>I-V graph</u>, by sticking them in the <u>formula</u> $R = V/I$.

The <u>gradient</u> (slope) of an <u>I-V graph</u> shows you how the resistance of the
component behaves. The <u>steeper</u> the graph the <u>lower</u> the resistance.

A <u>straight-line graph</u> has a constant gradient and shows a constant
resistance. If the graph <u>curves</u>, it means the resistance is <u>changing</u>.

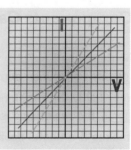
Keep going — the resistance
is lower the steeper it gets...

Four Hideously Important Current-Voltage Graphs

<u>Current-voltage</u> (*I-V*) <u>graphs</u> show how the current varies as you change the voltage.
Learn these <u>four</u> real well:

Wire

The current
through a <u>wire</u>
(at constant
temperature) is
<u>proportional to
voltage</u>.

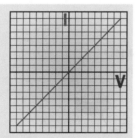

Different Resistors

The current through a
<u>resistor</u> (at constant
temperature) is
<u>proportional to voltage</u>.
<u>Different resistors</u> have
different <u>resistances</u>,
hence the different <u>slopes</u>.

Metal Filament Lamp

As the <u>temperature</u> of the
metal filament <u>increases</u>,
the <u>resistance increases</u>,
hence the <u>curve</u>.

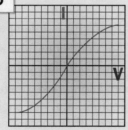

Diode

Current will only
flow through
a diode <u>in one
direction</u>, as
shown.

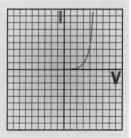

Revise this page — without any resistance...

Make sure you know how current, voltage and resistance are linked. You might need to draw an I-V graph in the exam,
or interpret one to find the resistance — make sure you can tell your lamp graphs from your diode graphs.

Q1   A 1.5 A current flows through a resistor when it is connected to a 9.0 V battery.
Calculate the resistance of the resistor.   [2 marks]

LDRs, Thermistors and LEDs

There are some really useful components that can be used in circuits to make all sorts of appliances work...

Circuit Symbols *You Should Know:*

You <u>will</u> need these for the <u>exam</u> — so learn them <u>now</u>.

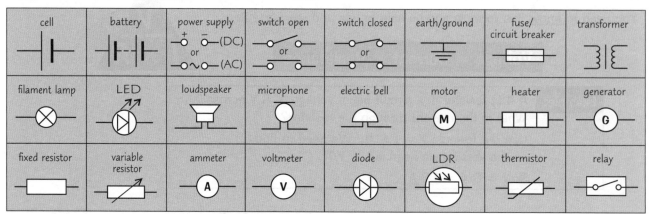

cell	battery	power supply	switch open	switch closed	earth/ground	fuse/ circuit breaker	transformer
filament lamp	LED	loudspeaker	microphone	electric bell	motor	heater	generator
fixed resistor	variable resistor	ammeter	voltmeter	diode	LDR	thermistor	relay

Light-Emitting Diodes are Really Useful

See page 17 for more on diodes.

1) <u>Light-emitting diodes</u> (LEDs) emit light when a current flows through them in the forward direction. They have lots of <u>practical applications</u>.

2) They are used for the numbers on <u>digital clocks</u>, in <u>traffic lights</u> and in <u>remote controls</u>.

3) Unlike a light bulb, they <u>don't have a filament that can burn out</u>.

> LEDs, like lamps, indicate the presence of <u>current</u> in a circuit. They are often used in appliances to show that they are switched on.

Some Components Can Change Resistance

1) A <u>light-dependent resistor</u> (LDR) is a special type of resistor that changes its resistance depending on how much light falls on it.

2) In <u>bright light</u>, the resistance <u>falls</u> and in <u>darkness</u>, the resistance is <u>highest</u>.

3) This makes it a useful device for various <u>electronic circuits</u>, e.g. <u>burglar detectors</u>.

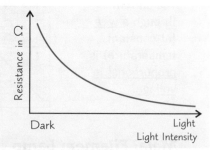

Resistance in Ω vs Light Intensity (Dark → Light)

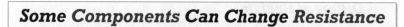

1) A <u>thermistor</u> is a temperature-dependent resistor.

2) In <u>hot</u> conditions, the resistance <u>drops</u> and in <u>cool</u> conditions, the resistance goes <u>up</u>.

3) Thermistors make useful <u>temperature detectors</u>, e.g. <u>car engine</u> temperature sensors, thermostats and fire alarms.

Resistance in Ω vs Temperature (Cold → Hot)

I'm a thermistor for ice cream — in heat my resistance drops...

LDRs and thermistors are useful little things. LDRs can be used for automatic light switches and in digital cameras. Thermistors can be used in thermostats and fire alarms.

Q1   A simple circuit consists of an thermistor and a battery connected in a single loop. Describe how the current in the circuit changes as the temperature of the thermistor increases.   **[3 marks]**

Series and Parallel Circuits

You can connect up circuits in two different ways — in <u>series</u> or in <u>parallel</u>. You need to know the differences between them, and be able to work out what sort of circuit should be used in <u>real-life</u> applications.

Series Circuits — All or Nothing

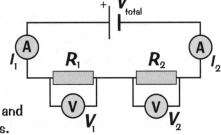

1) In <u>series circuits</u>, the different components are connected <u>in a line</u>, <u>end to end</u>, between the +ve and –ve of the power supply (except for <u>voltmeters</u>, which are always connected <u>in parallel</u>, but they don't count as part of the circuit).

2) If you remove or disconnect <u>one</u> component, the circuit is <u>broken</u> and they all <u>stop working</u>. This is generally <u>not very handy</u>, and in practice <u>only a few things</u> are connected in series, e.g. fairy lights.

3) For a <u>series</u> circuit:

- There's a bigger <u>supply p.d.</u> when more cells are in series (if they're all <u>connected</u> the <u>same way</u>). E.g. when two batteries with a p.d. of 1.5 V are <u>connected in series</u> they supply 3 V <u>between them</u>.
- The <u>current</u> is the <u>same everywhere</u>. $I_1 = I_2$ etc. The size of the current depends on the <u>total potential difference</u> and the <u>total resistance</u> of the circuit ($I = V_{total} \div R_{total}$).

  > p.d. = potential difference

- The total <u>potential difference</u> of the supply is <u>shared</u> between components. The p.d. for each component depends on its <u>resistance</u>.
- The <u>total resistance</u> of the circuit depends on the <u>number of components</u> and the <u>type</u> of components used. The <u>total resistance</u> is the <u>sum</u> of the resistance of <u>each component</u> in the circuit — $R_{total} = R_1 + R_2 + ...$

Parallel Circuits — Everything is Independent

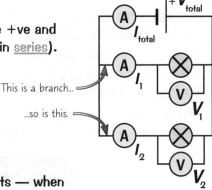

1) In <u>parallel circuits</u>, each component is <u>separately</u> connected to the +ve and –ve of the <u>supply</u> (except ammeters, which are <u>always</u> connected in <u>series</u>).

2) If you remove or disconnect <u>one</u> component, it will <u>hardly affect</u> the others at all.

This is a branch...

...so is this.

3) This is <u>obviously</u> how <u>most</u> things must be connected, for example in <u>cars</u> and in <u>household electrics</u>. Each <u>light switch</u> in your house is part of a branch of a parallel circuit — it just turns <u>one</u> light (or set of lights) on and off.

4) Everyday circuits often contain a <u>mixture</u> of series and parallel parts — when looking at components on the <u>same branch</u> the rules for <u>series</u> circuits apply.

5) For a <u>parallel</u> circuit:

- The <u>potential difference</u> is the <u>same</u> across all branches. $V_1 = V_2$ etc.
- <u>Current</u> is <u>shared</u> between <u>branches</u>. The <u>total current</u> flowing around the circuit is equal to the <u>total</u> of all the currents through the <u>separate components</u>. $I_{total} = I_1 + I_2$ etc.
- In a parallel circuit, there are <u>junctions</u> where the current either <u>splits</u> or <u>rejoins</u>. The total current going <u>into</u> a junction equals the total current <u>leaving</u> it, as charge can't just disappear or appear.
- The <u>current</u> through a branch depends on the <u>resistance</u> of the branch — the higher the resistance, the harder it is for charge to flow, and so the lower the current in that branch. If two <u>identical components</u> are connected in parallel then the <u>same current</u> will flow through each component.
- The <u>total resistance</u> of the circuit <u>decreases</u> if you add a second resistor in parallel.

Series circuits — they're no laughing matter...

Get those rules straightened out in your head, then have a go at these questions to test what you can remember.

Q1　Calculate the current in a series circuit containing a 12 V battery, a 7 Ω resistor and an 8 Ω resistor.　　[3 marks]

Charge, Voltage and Energy Change

Charge can be positive or negative — and when charge flows it is called current.

Charge Through a Circuit Depends on Current and Time

1) Current is the rate of flow of electrical charge (in amperes, A) around a circuit (see page 16).

2) In solid metal conductors (e.g. copper wire) charge is carried by negatively charged electrons.

3) When current (*I*) flows past a point in a circuit for a length of time (*t*) then the charge (*Q*) that has passed is given by this formula:

$$\text{Charge} = \text{Current} \times \text{Time}$$

$$\dfrac{Q}{I \times t}$$

4) More charge passes around a circuit when a bigger current flows.

Example: A battery charger passes a current of 2.5 A through a cell over a period of 4 hours.
How much charge does the charger transfer to the cell altogether?
$Q = I \times t = 2.5 \times (4 \times 60 \times 60) = \underline{36\ 000\ C}\ (\underline{36\ kC})$

The time needs to be in seconds.

Charge is measured in coulombs, C.

When a Charge Drops Through a Voltage it Transfers Energy

1) When an electrical charge (*Q*) goes through a change in voltage (*V*), then energy (*E*) is transferred.

2) Energy is supplied to the charge at the power source to 'raise' it through a voltage.

3) The charge gives up this energy when it 'falls' through any voltage drop in components elsewhere in the circuit.

4) The bigger the change in voltage, the more energy is transferred for a given amount of charge passing through the circuit.

5) That means that a battery with a bigger voltage will supply more energy to the circuit for every coulomb of charge which flows round it.

6) This is because the charge is raised up 'higher' at the start — and as the diagram shows, more energy will be dissipated in the circuit too.

Charges gaining energy at the battery

+6V

+6V

+3V

0V

0V

Battery

Charges releasing energy in resistors

$$\boxed{\text{Voltage is the energy transferred per unit charge passed}}$$

7) The unit for voltage, the volt, is defined as:

$$\boxed{\text{One volt is one joule per coulomb}}$$

8) You can calculate the energy transferred (in joules, J) to or from an amount of charge as it passes through a voltage using the equation:

$$\text{Energy transferred} = \text{Charge} \times \text{Voltage}$$

$$\dfrac{E}{Q \times V}$$

9) Combining this with $V = I \times R$ from page 17, you can also calculate the energy transferred by an amount of charge as it passes through a resistance using the equation:

$$\text{Energy transferred} = \text{Charge} \times \text{Current} \times \text{Resistance}$$

$$\dfrac{E}{Q \times I \times R}$$

Pole volting — athletics for electrons...

Make sure you know how voltage and energy transferred are linked — energy is transferred to and from a charge when it passes through a voltage difference. The diagram above is a useful one to remember...

Q1   Calculate the energy transferred to 10 000 C of charge as it passes through a 200 V source.   [2 marks]

Electrical Safety

Now then, did you know... electricity is dangerous. It can kill you. Well just watch out for it, that's all.

Appliances *must be* Earthed or Insulated

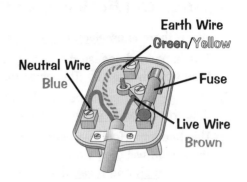

1) There are three wires in a plug — live, neutral and earth.

2) Only the live and neutral wires are usually needed, but if something goes wrong, the earth wire stops you getting hurt.

3) The LIVE WIRE alternates between a HIGH +VE AND –VE VOLTAGE of about 230 V.

4) The NEUTRAL WIRE is always at 0 V.

Positive can be written as +ve and negative as –ve.

5) Electricity normally flows in through the live wire and the neutral wire.

6) The EARTH WIRE and fuse (or circuit breaker) are just for safety and work together — see below.

All appliances with metal cases must be "earthed" to reduce the danger of electric shock. "Earthing" just means the case must be attached to an earth wire. An earthed conductor can never become live. If the appliance has a plastic casing and no metal parts showing then it's said to be double insulated. The plastic is an insulator, so it stops a current flowing — which means you can't get a shock. Anything with double insulation doesn't need an earth wire — just a live and neutral.

Earthing and Fuses *Prevent Fires and Shocks*

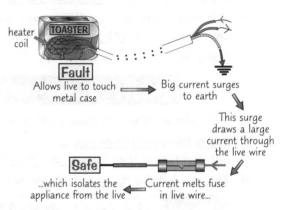

1) If a fault develops in which the live somehow touches the metal case, then because the case is earthed, a big current flows through the live wire, the case and the earth wire.

2) This surge in current 'blows' (melts) the fuse (or trips the circuit breaker — see below), which cuts off the live supply.

3) This isolates the whole appliance, making it impossible to get an electric shock from the case. It also prevents the risk of fire caused by the heating effect of a large current.

Circuit Breakers *Have Some Advantages Over Fuses*

1) Circuit breakers are an electrical safety device used in some circuits. Like fuses, they protect the circuit from damage if too much current flows.

2) When circuit breakers detect a surge in current in a circuit, they break the circuit by opening a switch.

3) A circuit breaker (and the circuit they're in) can easily be reset by flicking a switch on the device. This makes them more convenient than fuses — which have to be replaced once they've melted.

4) One common type of circuit breaker is a Residual Current Circuit Breaker (RCCB):

   a) Normally the same current flows through the live and neutral wires. If somebody touches the live wire, a current will flow through them to the earth. This means the neutral wire carries less current than the live wire. The RCCB detects this difference in current and cuts off the power by opening a switch.

   b) They also operate much faster than fuses — they break the circuit as soon as there is a current surge — no time is wasted waiting for the current to melt a fuse. This makes them safer.

   c) RCCBs even work for small current changes that might not be large enough to melt a fuse. Since even small currents could be fatal, this means RCCBs are more effective at protecting against electrocution.

Why are earth wires green and yellow — when mud's brown...

Electricity is very useful, but it can also be very dangerous. Make sure you know the risks.

Q1   State the wire of a plug that a fuse should be connected to.   [1 mark]

Energy and Power in Circuits

This page is all about how to cook toast... well, maybe not... but it's just as useful.

Resistors Get Hot When an Electric Current Passes Through Them

1) When there is an electric current in a resistor there is an energy transfer which heats the resistor.

2) This happens because the electrons collide with the ions in the lattice that make up the resistor as they flow through it. This gives the ions energy, which causes them to vibrate and heat up.

3) This heating effect increases the resistor's resistance — so less current will flow, or a greater voltage will be needed to produce the same current.

4) This heating effect can cause components in the circuit to melt — which means the circuit will stop working, or not work properly. Fuses use this effect to protect circuits — they melt and break the circuit if the current gets too high (see previous page).

5) The heating effect of an electric current can have other advantages. For example, it's ace if you want to heat something. Toasters contain a coil of wire with a really high resistance. When a current passes through the coil, its temperature increases so much that it glows and gives off infrared (heat) radiation which cooks the bread.

Electrical Power and Fuse Ratings

1) Electrical power is the rate at which an appliance transfers energy.

2) An appliance with a high power rating transfers a lot of energy in a short time.

3) This energy comes from the current flowing through it. This means that an appliance with a high power rating will draw a large current from the supply.

4) Power is measured in watts (W). The formula for electrical power is:

Electrical Power = Current × Voltage

$$\frac{P}{I \times V}$$

5) Most electrical goods show their power rating and voltage rating.

6) Fuses have current ratings and should be rated as near as possible but just higher than the normal operating current.

7) To work out the fuse needed, you need to work out the current that the item will normally use.

Example: A hair dryer is rated at 230 V, 1 kW. Find the fuse needed.
1 kW = 1000 W
$I = P/V = 1000/230 = 4.3$ A. Normally, the fuse should be rated just a little higher than the normal current, so a 5 amp fuse is ideal for this one.

The most common fuse ratings in the UK are 3 A, 5 A and 13 A.

Electrical Appliances Transfer Energy Electrically

1) The energy transferred by an appliance depends on the power of the appliance and how long it is on for (measured in seconds, s): Energy Transferred = Electrical Power × Time.

2) Using the equation above, the formula for energy transferred is:

Energy transferred = Current × voltage × time

$$\frac{E}{I \times V \times t}$$

Example: The motor in an electric toothbrush is attached to a 3 V battery. If a current of 0.8 A flows through the motor for 3 minutes, calculate the energy transferred by the motor.
Use $E = I \times V \times t = 0.8 \times 3 \times (3 \times 60) = \underline{432\text{ J}}$

Time needs to be in seconds.

Current = heat — so eat fruit cake when you're cold...

If a fuse's rating is too low, it will blow when you don't want it to. If it's too high, the fuse won't blow when it needs to.

Q1 Calculate the power of a lamp connected to a 230 V source with a 6.0 A current flowing through it. [2 marks]

Static Electricity

Static electricity is all about charges which are <u>not</u> free to move. This causes them to build up in one place and it often ends with a <u>spark</u> or a <u>shock</u> when they do finally move.

Like Charges Repel, Opposite Charges Attract

1) Two things with <u>opposite</u> electric charges are <u>attracted</u> to each other.
2) Two things with the <u>same</u> electric charge will <u>repel</u> each other.
3) These forces get <u>weaker</u> the <u>further apart</u> the two things are.

Conductors Conduct Charge — Insulators Don't

1) Materials that are <u>electrical conductors</u> conduct charge easily — a <u>current</u> can flow through them. They're usually <u>metals</u>, e.g. copper and silver.
2) <u>Electrical insulators</u> don't conduct charge very well — so a current can't flow. Examples include plastic and rubber.

A Static Charge Cannot Move

1) A <u>static charge</u> is a charge which <u>builds up</u> in one place and is <u>not free to move</u>. These are more common on <u>insulators</u>, where <u>current cannot flow</u>, rather than on <u>conductors</u>.
2) A common cause of static electricity is <u>friction</u> (see next page). When two <u>insulating</u> materials are <u>rubbed</u> together, electrons will be <u>scraped off one</u> and <u>dumped</u> on the other.
3) This'll leave a <u>positive</u> electrostatic charge on one and a <u>negative</u> electrostatic charge on the other.
4) <u>Which way</u> the electrons are transferred <u>depends</u> on the <u>two materials</u> involved.
5) Both +ve and −ve electrostatic charges are only ever produced by the movement of <u>electrons</u>. The positive charges <u>definitely do not move</u>! A positive static charge is always caused by electrons <u>moving</u> away elsewhere.
6) Static charges can occur on <u>conductors</u> too — cars often get a static charge on the outside because they've <u>gained</u> or <u>lost</u> electrons from the air rushing past them as they travel at high speeds.
7) A charged conductor can be <u>discharged safely</u> by connecting it to earth with a <u>metal strap</u>. The electrons flow <u>down</u> the strap to the ground if the charge is <u>negative</u> and flow <u>up</u> the strap from the ground if the charge is <u>positive</u>.

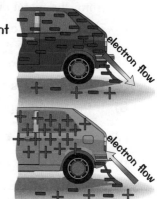

As Charge Builds Up, So Does the Voltage

1) As <u>electric charge</u> builds on an <u>isolated</u> object, the <u>voltage</u> between the object and the earth (which is at zero volts) <u>increases</u>.
2) If the voltage gets large enough, electrons can <u>jump</u> across the gap between the charged object and the earth — this is the <u>spark</u>.
3) They can also jump to any <u>earthed conductor</u> that is nearby — which is why you can get <u>static shocks</u> from clothes, or getting out of a car.
4) This <u>usually</u> happens when the gap is fairly <u>small</u>. (But not always — <u>lightning</u> is just a really big spark, see page 25.)

Static caravans — where electrons go on holiday...

Static electricity's great fun. You must have tried it — rubbing a balloon against your jumper and trying to get it to stick to the ceiling. It really works... well, sometimes. Bad hair days are caused by static too — it builds up on your hair, so your strands of hair repel each other. Which is nice...

Q1 Jake removes his jumper in a dark room. As he does so, he hears a crackling noise and sees tiny sparks of light between his jumper and his shirt. Explain the cause of this. [3 marks]

Static Electricity and Friction

You can test whether an object is <u>charged</u>, and whether the charge is <u>positive</u> or <u>negative</u>, by looking for <u>attraction</u> and <u>repulsion</u>.

Investigating Static Electricity   PRACTICAL

1) As you saw on the previous page, <u>static charges</u> can be caused by <u>friction</u>.

2) The classic examples of this are <u>polythene</u> and <u>acetate</u> rods being rubbed with a <u>cloth duster</u>, as shown in the diagrams. You can test these out for yourself <u>in the lab</u>.

3) When the <u>polythene rod</u> is rubbed with the duster, electrons move <u>from the duster</u> to the rod. The <u>rod</u> becomes <u>negatively charged</u> and the <u>duster</u> is left with an <u>equal positive charge</u>.

4) When the <u>acetate rod</u> is rubbed, electrons move <u>from the rod</u> to the duster. The <u>duster</u> becomes <u>negatively charged</u> and the <u>rod</u> is left with an <u>equal positive charge</u>.

5) You can confirm that these rods have become charged using the methods outlined below.

1) Gold-Leaf Electroscope

1) You can see whether a material is <u>charged</u> by using a <u>gold-leaf electroscope</u>.

2) A gold-leaf electroscope has a <u>metal disc</u> connected to a <u>metal rod</u>, at the bottom of which are attached two thin pieces of <u>gold leaf</u>.

3) When a rod with a <u>charge</u> is brought near to the disc of the electroscope, <u>electrons</u> will either be <u>attracted</u> to, or <u>repelled</u> from, the metal disc — depending on the charge of the rod.

4) This induces a charge in the <u>metal disc</u>, which in turn induces a charge in the <u>gold leaves</u>. Both gold leaves will have the <u>same charge</u>, so they will <u>repel</u> each other, causing them to <u>rise</u>.

5) When the rod is taken away, the gold leaves will <u>discharge</u> and <u>fall</u> again.

6) If the foil <u>does not rise</u> when the rod is brought near the disc, the rod is <u>not charged</u>.

2) Suspending a Charged Rod

1) Another way of testing whether a rod of material is charged is to <u>suspend</u> a rod with a <u>known charge</u> on a thread and see if there is <u>repulsion</u> or <u>attraction</u> when the rod you're testing is brought close to it.

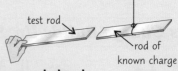

2) If there is an <u>attraction</u>, then the <u>test rod</u> has the <u>opposite</u> charge to the suspended rod.

3) If there is a <u>repulsion</u>, then the test rod has the <u>same</u> charge as the suspended rod.

Van de Graaff Generators Make Your Hair Stand on End

A <u>Van de Graaff generator</u> is used to demonstrate electrostatic charges. It's made up of a <u>rubber belt</u> moving round <u>plastic rollers</u> underneath a <u>metal dome</u>. An electrostatic charge is built up on the metal dome as the belt goes round. If you stand on an <u>insulated</u> chair and place your hands on the dome, electrons will move between your body and the dome, giving your body a charge. The human body <u>conducts charge</u>, and <u>like</u> charges <u>repel</u>, so the charges will <u>spread out</u> as much as possible throughout your body. The charge is strong enough to make your hairs <u>repel</u> each other and stand on end.

This page is completely free of charge — hopefully...

Use these experiments to investigate how different things become charged depending on what they're made of.

Q1   Describe one way of demonstrating that an insulating object is carrying a static charge.   [2 marks]

Static Electricity — Examples

They like asking you to give <u>quite detailed examples</u> in exams. Make sure you <u>learn all these details</u>.

Static Electricity Being Helpful:

1) Inkjet Printer

1) Tiny droplets of ink are forced out of a <u>fine nozzle</u>, making them <u>electrically charged</u>.

2) The droplets are <u>deflected</u> as they pass between two metal plates. A <u>voltage</u> is applied to the plates — one is <u>negative</u> and the other is <u>positive</u>.

3) The droplets are <u>attracted</u> to the plate of the <u>opposite</u> charge and <u>repelled</u> from the plate with the <u>same</u> charge.

4) The <u>size</u> and <u>direction</u> of the voltage across each plate changes so each droplet is deflected to hit a <u>different place</u> on the paper.

5) Loads of <u>tiny dots</u> make up your printout. Clever.

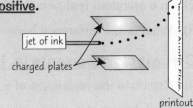

2) Photocopier

1) The <u>image plate</u> is positively charged. An image of what you're copying is projected onto it.

2) Whiter bits of what you're copying make <u>light</u> fall on the plate and the charge <u>leaks away</u> in those places.

3) The charged bits attract negatively charged <u>black powder</u>, which is transferred onto positively charged paper.

4) The paper is <u>heated</u> so the powder sticks.

5) Voilà, a <u>photocopy</u> of your piece of paper (or whatever else you've shoved in there).

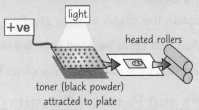

Static Electricity Being a Little Joker:

Clothing Crackles

When <u>synthetic clothes</u> are <u>dragged</u> over each other (like in a <u>tumble dryer</u>) or over your <u>head</u>, electrons get scraped off, leaving <u>static charges</u> on both parts, and that leads to the inevitable — <u>attraction</u> (they stick together) and little <u>sparks</u> / <u>shocks</u> as the charges <u>rearrange themselves</u>.

Static Electricity Being a Serious Problem:

1) Lightning

Rain drops and ice <u>bump together</u> inside storm clouds, knocking off electrons and leaving the top of the cloud positively charged and the bottom of the cloud <u>negative</u>. This creates a <u>huge voltage</u> and a <u>big spark</u>.

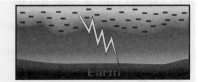

2) The Fuel-Filling Nightmare

1) As <u>fuel</u> flows out of a <u>filler pipe</u>, <u>static can build up</u>.

2) This can easily lead to a <u>spark</u> and in <u>dusty</u> or <u>fumy</u> places — <u>BOOM!</u>

3) <u>The solution</u>: make the nozzles out of <u>metal</u> so that the charge is <u>conducted away</u>, instead of building up.

4) It's also good to have <u>earthing straps</u> between the <u>fuel tank</u> and the <u>fuel pipe</u>.

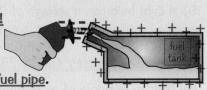

I know, I know — yet another shocking joke...

Lightning always chooses the easiest path to get to the ground — even if that means going through tall buildings and trees. That's why you should never put up an umbrella or fly a kite in a thunderstorm.

Q1   Give an example of a device that uses static electricity.   [1 mark]

Paper 2

Paper 2

Revision Questions for Section 2

And you've struggled through to the end of Section 2. Have a break, then test what you can remember.
- Try these questions and tick off each one when you get it right.
- When you've done all the questions for a topic and are completely happy with it, tick off the topic.

Circuit Properties (p.16) ☑

1) Explain what current, voltage and resistance are in an electric circuit. ☑
2) In a standard test circuit, where must the ammeter be placed? Where must the voltmeter be placed? ☑
3) What is the difference between a.c. and d.c.? ☑

Circuit Components (p.17-18) ☑

4) Calculate the resistance of a wire if the voltage across it is 12 V and the current through it is 2.5 A. ☑
5) Sketch typical current-voltage graphs for:

a) a wire (at constant temperature),

b) a resistor (at constant temperature),

c) a filament lamp,

d) a diode.

Explain the shape of each graph. ☑
6) What can LEDs be used to indicate the presence of? ☑
7) Describe how the resistance of an LDR varies with light intensity. Give an application of an LDR. ☑

Series and Parallel Circuits (p.19) ☑

8) True or False? The current is the same everywhere in a series circuit. ☑
9) Why are parallel circuits often more useful than series ones? ☑

Electrical Safety and Energy in Circuits (p.20-22) ☑

10) If 80 C of charge is carried past a certain point in a wire in 2 s, how much current is flowing? ☑
11) Give the definition of a volt. ☑
12) Sketch a properly wired three-pin plug. ☑
13) What does it mean if an appliance is 'double insulated'? ☑
14) Explain how a fuse and earth wire work together in a plug. ☑
15) Explain how a Residual Current Circuit Breaker (RCCB) works. ☑
16) Give two advantages of using an RCCB instead of a fuse and an earthing wire. ☑
17) Why does the wire in a fuse melt when the current gets too high? ☑
18) Find the appropriate fuse (3 A, 5 A or 13 A) for these appliances:

a) a toaster rated at 230 V, 1100 W   b) an electric heater rated at 230 V, 2000 W ☑
19) A light bulb has a voltage of 20 V across it and 7.2 kJ of energy is transferred to it electrically over a 2 minute period. What current flows through the bulb? ☑

Static Electricity (p.23-25) ☑

20) Give an example of an electrical conductor and an electrical insulator. ☑
21) What causes the build-up of static electricity? Which particles move when static builds up? ☑
22) Describe how an acetate rod becomes electrically charged when it is rubbed with a duster. ☑
23) Give two examples of how static electricity can be dangerous. ☑

Waves — The Basics

We're constantly bombarded by waves (light, sound, heat)... and they've all got stuff in common.

All Waves Have Wavelength, Frequency, Amplitude and Speed

1) WAVELENGTH (λ) is the distance from one peak to the next.

2) FREQUENCY (f) is how many complete waves there are per second (passing a certain point).
It's measured in hertz (Hz). 1 Hz is 1 wave per second.

3) AMPLITUDE is the height of the wave (from rest to crest).

4) The SPEED (v, for velocity) is, well, how fast the wave goes.

5) The PERIOD (T) is the time it takes (in s) for one complete wave to pass a point.
E.g. a wave with period 0.002 s has a frequency of 1 ÷ 0.002 = 500 Hz.

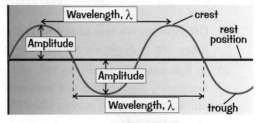

$$f = \frac{1}{T}$$

Wave Speed = Frequency × Wavelength

1) You need to learn this equation — and practise using it.

$$\text{Speed} = \text{Frequency} \times \text{Wavelength}$$
$$\text{(m/s)} \qquad \text{(Hz)} \qquad \text{(m)}$$

OR

$$v = f \times \lambda$$

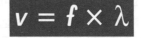

2) You won't always be asked for the speed though, so you might need this triangle too...

> EXAMPLE: Find the frequency of a light wave with wavelength 1×10^{-7} m. (Speed of light = 3×10^8 m/s.)
> Using the triangle, frequency = speed ÷ wavelength = $(3 \times 10^8) \div (1 \times 10^{-7})$ = $\underline{3 \times 10^{15}}$ Hz.

3) Waves often have high frequencies which are given in awkward units like kHz or MHz:
1 kHz (kilohertz) = 1000 Hz, and 1 MHz (megahertz) = 1 000 000 Hz.
For example, 900 MHz = 900 000 000 Hz.

Waves Can Be Transverse or Longitudinal

Most waves are TRANSVERSE:
1) Light and all other EM waves (see p.28).
2) A slinky spring wiggled up and down.
3) Waves on strings.
4) Ripples on water.

In TRANSVERSE waves the vibrations are at 90° to the DIRECTION ENERGY IS TRANSFERRED by the wave.

Some LONGITUDINAL waves are:
1) Sound and ultrasound.
2) Shock waves, e.g. some seismic waves.
3) A slinky spring when you push the end.

In LONGITUDINAL waves the vibrations are along the SAME DIRECTION as the wave transfers energy.

All Waves Transfer Energy and Information Without Transferring Matter

1) All waves carry and transfer energy in the direction they're travelling. E.g. microwaves in an oven make things warm up — their energy is transferred to the food you're cooking. Sound waves can make things vibrate or move, e.g. loud bangs can start avalanches.

2) Waves can also be used as signals to transfer information from one place to another — e.g. light in optical fibres, or radio waves travelling through the air. There's more on this on page 29.

Lambda nsak — waves & lentils...

Make sure you remember that light is a transverse wave and that sound waves are longitudinal. It's important.

Q1   A sound wave in a material has a frequency of 19 kHz and a wavelength of 12.5 cm. Find its speed.   [1 mark]

Wave Behaviour and EM Waves

The properties you saw on the last page can affect how waves <u>behave</u>. There's one type of wave which has very <u>different properties</u> at different wavelengths — we call these waves <u>electromagnetic</u>...

Two or More Waves Moving Together Have Wavefronts

1) Often when we talk about waves approaching an obstacle or boundary, there are <u>multiple</u> waves moving together in the same direction.

2) In this case it's useful to talk about <u>wavefronts</u>. Wavefronts are imaginary <u>planes</u> that cut across all the waves, connecting the points on adjacent waves which are <u>vibrating together</u>.

3) The distance between each wavefront is equal to <u>one wavelength</u>, i.e. each wavefront is at the <u>same point</u> in the <u>cycle</u>.

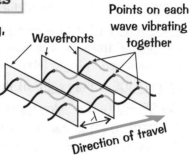

The Doppler Effect Makes Waves Longer or Shorter

1) The waves produced by a source which is moving <u>towards</u> or <u>away</u> from an observer will have a <u>different wavelength</u> than they would if the source were <u>stationary</u>.

2) This is because the <u>wave speed</u> is <u>constant</u>, so if the source is moving, it 'catches up' to the waves in front of it. This causes the wavefronts to <u>bunch up</u> in front of the moving source and <u>spread out</u> behind it.

3) The <u>frequency</u> of a wave from a source moving <u>towards</u> you will be <u>higher</u> and its <u>wavelength</u> will be <u>shorter</u> than the wave produced by the source.

4) The <u>frequency</u> of a wave from a source moving <u>away</u> from you will be <u>lower</u> and its <u>wavelength</u> will be <u>longer</u> than the wave produced by the source.

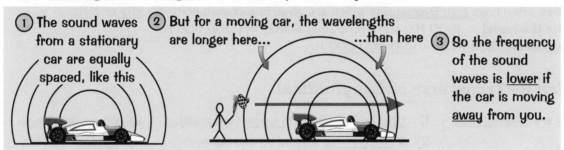

5) The <u>faster</u> a wave is moving away from you, the <u>longer</u> its wavelength will be.

There are Seven Types of Electromagnetic (EM) Waves

1) <u>Electromagnetic</u> (EM) waves with <u>different wavelengths</u> have different properties. They're grouped into <u>seven</u> types depending on their wavelength. But the types actually merge to form a <u>continuous spectrum</u>.

RADIO WAVES	MICRO-WAVES	INFRA-RED	VISIBLE LIGHT	ULTRA-VIOLET	X-RAYS	GAMMA RAYS
$1\,m - 10^4\,m$	$10^{-2}\,m$ (1 cm)	$10^{-5}\,m$ (0.01 mm)	$10^{-7}\,m$	$10^{-8}\,m$	$10^{-10}\,m$	$10^{-12}\,m$

Wavelength →

INCREASING FREQUENCY AND DECREASING WAVELENGTH

2) All types of EM radiation are <u>transverse</u> waves and travel at the <u>same speed through free space</u> (a vacuum).

3) The different <u>colours</u> of <u>visible light</u> depend on the <u>wavelength</u> — red has the <u>longest wavelength</u> (and <u>lowest frequency</u>) and <u>violet</u> has the <u>shortest wavelength</u> (and <u>highest frequency</u>).

Infrared and yellow and pink and green...

You need to know the colours <u>in order</u> of increasing frequency (decreasing wavelength) so just remember: <u>R</u>ichard <u>O</u>f <u>Y</u>ork <u>G</u>ave <u>B</u>attle <u>I</u>n <u>V</u>ain (<u>red</u>, <u>orange</u>, <u>yellow</u>, <u>green</u>, <u>blue</u>, <u>indigo</u>, <u>violet</u>).

Q1 An ambulance travels towards you, passes and then continues travelling away. Compare the observed frequency of the siren before and after the ambulance passes. Give the name of this phenomenon. [2 marks]

Uses of Electromagnetic Waves

Waves are <u>brilliant</u> — there's so much you can do with a wave. So let's have a closer look at the <u>uses</u> of <u>EM waves</u>.

Radio Waves are Used Mainly for Communications

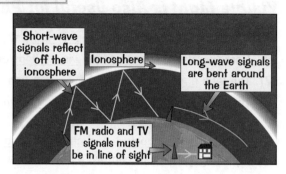

1) <u>Radio waves</u> are EM radiation with wavelengths longer than about 10 cm.

2) <u>Long-wave radio</u> (wavelengths of <u>1 – 10 km</u>) can be transmitted a long way because long wavelengths are bent around the curved surface of the Earth.

3) <u>Short-wave radio</u> signals (wavelengths of about <u>10 m – 100 m</u>) can also be received at <u>long distances</u> from the transmitter. That's because they are <u>reflected</u> from the <u>ionosphere</u> (a layer of the Earth's atmosphere).

4) The radio waves used for <u>TV and FM radio broadcasting</u> have very short wavelengths (10 cm – 10 m). To get reception, you must be in <u>direct sight of the transmitter</u> — the signal doesn't bend around hills.

Microwaves are Used for Satellite Communication and Heating Food

1) Microwaves have a wavelength of around <u>1 – 10 cm</u>, and can also be used for communication.

2) <u>Satellite communication</u> (including <u>satellite TV</u> signals and <u>satellite phones</u>) uses microwaves.

3) For satellite TV, the signal from a <u>transmitter</u> is transmitted into space, where it's picked up by the satellite receiver dish <u>orbiting</u> thousands of kilometres above the Earth. The satellite <u>transmits</u> the signal back to Earth where it's received by a <u>satellite dish</u> on the ground.

4) Mobile phone calls also travel as <u>microwaves</u> from your phone to the nearest <u>transmitter</u>.

5) Microwaves are also used for <u>cooking</u>. These microwaves are <u>absorbed</u> by the water molecules in the food. They penetrate a few centimetres into the food before being <u>absorbed</u>. The energy is then <u>conducted</u> or <u>convected</u> to other parts (see pages 43-44) of the food.

Infrared Radiation is Used for Heating and to Monitor Temperature

1) <u>Infrared</u> radiation (or IR) is also known as <u>heat radiation</u>. Electrical <u>heaters</u> radiate IR to keep us <u>warm</u>, and things like <u>grills</u> use IR to <u>cook food</u>.

2) IR is <u>given out</u> by <u>all objects</u> — the <u>hotter</u> the object, the <u>more</u> IR radiation it gives out.

3) The infrared radiation given out by objects can be detected in the dark of night by <u>night-vision equipment</u>. The equipment turns it into an <u>electrical signal</u>, which is <u>displayed on a screen</u> as a picture, allowing things which would otherwise be <u>hidden</u> in the dark (e.g. <u>criminals</u> on the run) to be <u>seen</u>.

Light Signals Can Travel Through Optical Fibres

This is known as total internal reflection — see p. 35.

1) As well as using it to <u>look at things</u> around us, <u>visible light</u> can be used for communication using <u>optical fibres</u> — which carry <u>data</u> over long distances as <u>pulses</u> of <u>light</u>.

2) Optical fibres work by <u>bouncing waves</u> off the sides of a very narrow <u>core</u>.

3) The pulse of light <u>enters the fibre</u> at a <u>certain angle</u> at one end and is reflected <u>again and again</u> until it emerges at the other end.

4) Optical fibres are increasingly being used for <u>telephone</u> and <u>broadband internet cables</u>. They're also used for <u>medical</u> purposes to '<u>see inside</u>' the body without having to operate.

Microwaves — used for TV AND for TV dinners...

...and for texting your mum to ask her to record your favourite programme. See — I told you waves were ace.

Q1   Give two uses of infrared radiation.   [2 marks]

Uses of Electromagnetic Waves

That's right — <u>yet another page</u> on the <u>uses of EM waves</u>. <u>Visible light</u>, <u>ultraviolet</u>, <u>X-rays</u> and <u>gamma rays</u> are the <u>shortest</u> waves in the spectrum, and we use them for <u>all sorts</u> of fancy stuff...

Visible Light is Also Useful for Photography

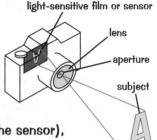

It sounds pretty obvious, but <u>photography</u> would be kinda <u>tricky</u> without visible light.

1) Cameras use a <u>lens</u> to focus <u>visible light</u> onto a light-sensitive <u>film</u> or <u>sensor</u>.
2) The lens <u>aperture</u> controls <u>how much</u> light enters the camera.
3) The <u>shutter speed</u> determines <u>how long</u> the film or sensor is <u>exposed</u> to the light.
4) By varying the <u>aperture</u> and <u>shutter speed</u> (and also the <u>sensitivity</u> of the film or the sensor), a photographer can capture as much or as little light as they want in their photograph.

Ultraviolet is Used in Fluorescent Lamps

1) <u>Fluorescence</u> is a property of certain chemicals, where <u>ultraviolet radiation (UV)</u> is <u>absorbed</u> and then <u>visible light</u> is <u>emitted</u>. That's why fluorescent colours look so bright — they actually emit light.

The Sun also emits a lot of UV radiation — it can cause damage to skin cells (see p.31).

2) <u>Fluorescent lights</u> (like the ones you might have in your classroom) use UV radiation to <u>emit</u> visible light. They're safe to use as <u>nearly all</u> the UV radiation is <u>absorbed</u> by a phosphor coating on the inside of the glass which emits <u>visible light</u> instead.
3) Fluorescent lights are more <u>energy-efficient</u> (see page 40) than filament light bulbs.

X-Rays Let Us See Inside Things

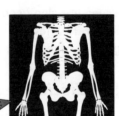

1) X-rays are used to view the <u>internal structure</u> of objects and materials, including our <u>bodies</u> — which is why they're so useful in <u>medicine</u>.
2) To make an X-ray image, X-rays are directed through the object or body onto a <u>detector plate</u>. The <u>brighter bits</u> are where <u>fewer X-rays</u> get through. This is a <u>negative image</u>.

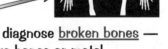

3) Radiographers in hospitals take X-ray photographs to help doctors diagnose <u>broken bones</u> — X-rays pass easily through <u>flesh</u> but not through <u>denser material</u> like bones or metal.
4) Exposure to X-rays can cause <u>mutations</u> which lead to <u>cancer</u>, so radiographers and patients are protected as much as possible by <u>lead aprons</u> and <u>shields</u>, and exposure to the radiation is kept to a <u>minimum</u>.

Gamma Radiation Can be Very Useful For...

...Sterilising Medical Equipment

1) Gamma rays are used to <u>sterilise</u> medical instruments by <u>killing</u> all the microbes.
2) This is better than trying to <u>boil</u> plastic instruments, which might be <u>damaged</u> by high temperatures.

...Sterilising Food

1) <u>Food</u> can be sterilised in the same way as medical instruments — again <u>killing</u> all the <u>microbes</u>.
2) This keeps the food <u>fresh for longer</u>, without having to freeze it or cook it or preserve it some other way.
3) The food is <u>not</u> radioactive afterwards, so it's <u>perfectly safe</u> to eat.

Lights. Camera. Action...

You've probably got the idea by now that we use electromagnetic radiation an awful lot — much more even than the few examples covered on these pages. These are the uses you need to make sure you know for the exam though.

Q1 Suggest one advantage of using gamma rays to sterilise medical instruments instead of boiling them. [1 mark]

Dangers of Electromagnetic Waves

Okay, so you know how useful electromagnetic radiation can be — well, it can also be pretty <u>dangerous</u>. (So it'll probably be banned one of these days... sigh.)

Some EM Radiation Can be Harmful to People

When EM radiation enters <u>living tissue</u> — like <u>you</u> — it's often harmless, but sometimes it creates havoc.

1) Some EM radiation mostly <u>passes through soft tissue</u> without being absorbed — e.g. radio waves.

2) Other types of radiation are absorbed and cause <u>heating</u> of the cells — e.g. microwaves.

3) Some radiations can cause <u>cancerous changes</u> in living cells — e.g. gamma rays can cause cancer.

Higher Frequency EM Radiation is Usually More Dangerous

1) The <u>effects</u> of <u>EM radiation</u> depend on its <u>frequency</u>. The higher the <u>frequency</u> of EM radiation, the more <u>energy</u> it has and generally the more <u>harmful</u> it can be.

2) In general, waves with <u>lower frequencies</u> (like <u>radio waves</u> — which are <u>harmless</u> as far as we know) are <u>less harmful</u> than <u>high frequency</u> waves like X-rays and gamma rays.

3) From a <u>safety</u> point of view, it's how radiation affects <u>human tissue</u> that's most vital. You need to know how the <u>body</u> can be affected if exposed to too much of the following radiation:

INCREASING FREQUENCY

MICROWAVES

<u>Microwaves</u> have a <u>similar frequency</u> to the <u>vibrations</u> of many <u>molecules</u>, and so they can increase these vibrations. The result is <u>internal heating</u> — the heating of molecules inside things (as in <u>microwave ovens</u>). Microwaves <u>HEAT HUMAN BODY TISSUE</u> internally in this way.

<u>Microwave ovens</u> need to have <u>shielding</u> to prevent microwaves from reaching the user.

INFRARED

The <u>infrared</u> (IR) range of frequencies can make the <u>surface molecules</u> of any substance <u>vibrate</u> — and like microwaves, this has a <u>heating effect</u>. But infrared has a <u>higher frequency</u>, so it carries <u>more energy</u> than microwave radiation. If the <u>human body</u> is exposed to <u>too much infrared</u> radiation, it can cause some nasty <u>SKIN BURNS</u>. You can protect yourself using insulating materials to reduce the amount of IR reaching your skin.

ULTRAVIOLET

UV radiation can <u>DAMAGE SURFACE CELLS</u> and cause <u>BLINDNESS</u>. Some frequencies of UV radiation are 'ionising' — they carry <u>enough energy</u> to knock electrons off atoms. This can cause <u>cell mutation or destruction</u>, and cancer.

You should wear sunscreen with <u>UV filters</u> whenever you're out in the sun, and stay out of <u>strong sunlight</u> to protect your skin from UV radiation.

GAMMA

<u>Very high-frequency</u> waves, such as <u>gamma rays</u>, are also <u>ionising</u>, and carry <u>much more energy</u> than UV rays. This means they can be <u>much more damaging</u> and they can <u>penetrate further</u> into the body. Like all ionising radiation, they can cause <u>CELL MUTATION</u> or <u>destruction</u>, leading to <u>TISSUE DAMAGE</u> or <u>CANCER</u>.

Radioactive sources of gamma rays should be kept in <u>lead-lined boxes</u> when not in use. When people need to be exposed to them, e.g. in medical treatment, the exposure time should be as <u>short</u> as possible.

I'll have the gamma and chips please, save the pineapple...

There's no point being paranoid — a little bit of sunshine won't kill you (in fact it'll probably do you good). But don't be daft... getting cancer from sunbathing for hours on end is no laughing matter. It's all a case of balancing the risks against the benefits, as well as keeping unnecessary exposure to a minimum.

Q1 Explain why gamma rays are more dangerous to humans than visible light. [2 marks]

Reflection and Refraction of Waves

All waves can be <u>reflected</u> or <u>refracted</u>. Reflection happens when light <u>bounces</u> off an even surface, and <u>refraction</u> occurs when a wave slows down or speeds up at a boundary between two materials.

Reflection of Light Lets Us See Things

1) <u>Visible light</u> is a <u>transverse</u> wave (see page 27), like all EM waves.

2) <u>Reflection of visible light</u> is what allows us to see most objects. Light bounces off them into our eyes.

3) When light reflects from an <u>uneven surface</u> such as a piece of paper, the light reflects off at all different angles and you get a <u>diffuse reflection</u>.

4) When light reflects from an <u>even surface</u> (smooth and shiny like a mirror) then it's all reflected at the <u>same angle</u> and you get a <u>clear reflection</u>.

5) But don't forget, the <u>LAW OF REFLECTION</u> applies to every reflected ray:

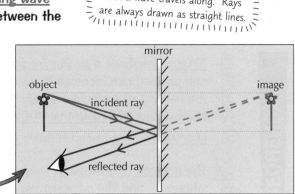

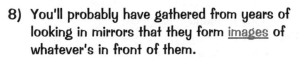

Angle of incidence = Angle of reflection

6) The <u>normal</u> is an imaginary line that's <u>perpendicular</u> (at right angles) to the surface at the <u>point of incidence</u> (the point where the wave hits the boundary). The normal is usually shown as a <u>dotted line</u>.

7) The <u>angle of incidence</u> is the angle between the <u>incoming wave</u> and the <u>normal</u>. The <u>angle of reflection</u> is the angle between the <u>reflected wave</u> and the <u>normal</u>.

A ray diagram shows the path that a wave travels along. Rays are always drawn as straight lines.

8) You'll probably have gathered from years of looking in mirrors that they form <u>images</u> of whatever's in front of them.

9) <u>Virtual images</u> are formed when the light rays bouncing off an object onto a mirror are <u>diverging</u>, so the light from the object appears to be coming from a completely different place. This ray diagram shows how an <u>image</u> is formed in a <u>PLANE MIRROR</u>.

Waves Can be Refracted

1) Waves travel at <u>different speeds</u> in substances which have <u>different densities</u>. EM waves travel more <u>slowly</u> in <u>denser</u> media (usually). Sound waves travel faster in <u>denser</u> substances.

2) So when a wave crosses a boundary between two substances, from glass to air, say, it <u>changes speed</u>.

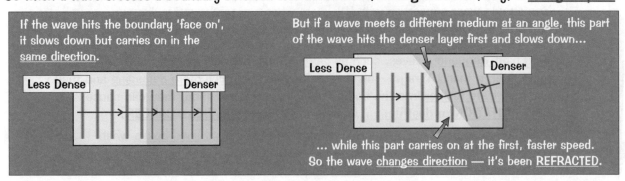

If the wave hits the boundary 'face on', it slows down but carries on in the <u>same direction</u>.

But if a wave meets a different medium <u>at an angle</u>, this part of the wave hits the denser layer first and slows down...

Less Dense   Denser

Less Dense   Denser

... while this part carries on at the first, faster speed. So the wave <u>changes direction</u> — it's been <u>REFRACTED</u>.

Plane mirrors — what pilots use to look behind them...

This stuff on reflection ain't too complicated — and it's easy marks in the exam. Make sure you can scribble down some nice, clear ray diagrams and you should be well on your way to a great mark.

Q1   A ray is incident on a plane mirror at an angle of incidence of 25°.
      What is the angle of reflection of the ray?   [1 mark]

More About Refraction of Waves

Didn't get your fill of refraction from the last page? Don't worry, we've got you covered...

Draw a Ray Diagram for a Refracted Wave

A ray diagram shows the path that a wave travels. You can draw one for a refracted light ray:

1) First, start by drawing the boundary between your two materials and the normal (a line that is at 90° to the boundary).

2) Draw an incident ray that meets the normal at the boundary.

3) The angle between the ray and the normal is the angle of incidence. (If you're given this angle, make sure to draw it carefully using a protractor.)

4) Now draw the refracted ray on the other side of the boundary. If the second material is denser than the first, the refracted ray bends towards the normal (like on the right). The angle between the refracted ray and the normal (the angle of refraction) is smaller than the angle of incidence.

5) If the second material is less dense, the angle of refraction is larger than the angle of incidence.

There are more ray diagrams on p.34.

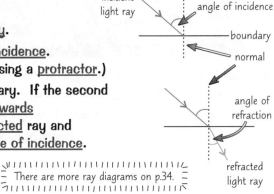

Rays Passing Through a Glass Block are Refracted Twice PRACTICAL

1) You can experiment with refraction using a light source and a rectangular block of a particular material (e.g. glass) resting on top of a piece of paper...

2) Shine a light ray at an angle into the block, as shown. Some of the light is reflected, but a lot of it passes through the glass and gets refracted as it does so.

3) Trace the incident and emergent rays onto the piece of paper and remove the block. You can draw in the refracted ray through the block by joining the ends of the other two rays with a straight line.

4) You should see that as the light passes from the air into the block (a denser medium), it bends towards the normal. This is because it slows down.

5) When the light reaches the boundary on the other side of the block, it's passing into a less dense medium. So it speeds up and bends away from the normal. (Some of the light is also reflected at this boundary.)

6) The light ray that emerges on the other side of the block is now travelling in the same direction it was to begin with — it's been refracted towards the normal and then back again by the same amount.

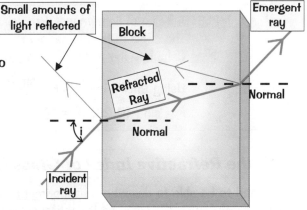

Triangular Prisms Disperse White Light PRACTICAL

You'll get an interesting effect if you shine white light into a triangular prism. Different wavelengths of light refract by different amounts, so white light (which is a mixture of all visible frequencies) disperses into different colours as it enters a prism and the different wavelengths are refracted by different amounts. A similar effect happens as the light leaves the prism, which means you get a nice rainbow effect.

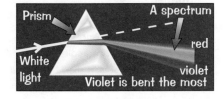

Denser media — lead newspapers...

Learn the straightforward rule: more dense materials slow light down, less dense materials speed it up.

Q1   A ray travels from a less dense material to a more dense one. The angle of incidence is 30°. The angle of refraction at the boundary is 20°. Sketch the ray diagram for this ray.   [2 marks]

Refractive Index and Snell's Law

So you're <u>totally happy</u> with the last two pages. And you're <u>sure</u> about that. Good. Gets a bit hairy here...

Every Transparent Material Has a Refractive Index

1) The <u>refractive index</u> of a <u>transparent material</u> tells you <u>how fast</u> light travels in that material. The <u>refractive index</u> of a material is defined as:

$$\text{refractive index, } n = \frac{\text{speed of light in a vacuum, } c}{\text{speed of light in that material, } v} \qquad n = \frac{c}{v}$$

2) Light <u>slows down a lot</u> in <u>glass</u>, so the <u>refractive index</u> of glass is <u>high</u> (around 1.5). The refractive index of <u>water</u> is a bit <u>lower</u> (around 1.33) — so light doesn't slow down as much in water as in glass.

3) The <u>speed of light in air</u> is about the <u>same</u> as in a <u>vacuum</u>, so the <u>refractive index</u> of <u>air</u> is 1.00 (to 2 d.p.).

4) According to Snell's law, the <u>angle of incidence</u>, <u>angle of refraction</u> and <u>refractive index</u> are all <u>linked</u>...

Snell's Law Says...

When an incident ray passes into a material:

$$n = \frac{\sin i}{\sin r}$$

So if you know <u>any two</u> of <u>n</u>, <u>i</u> or <u>r</u>, you can work out the <u>missing one</u>.

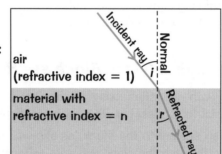
air (refractive index = 1)
material with refractive index = n
Incident ray   Normal   Refracted ray   i   r

Remember, if a wave is travelling along (or parallel to) the normal when it crosses a boundary between materials, it doesn't refract.

EXAMPLE: A beam of light travels from air into water.
The angle of incidence is 23°. Refractive index of water = 1.33.
Calculate the angle of refraction to the nearest degree.

Using Snell's law, $\sin r = \dfrac{\sin i}{n} = \dfrac{\sin 23°}{1.33} = 0.29...$
$r = \sin^{-1}(0.29...) = \underline{17°}$

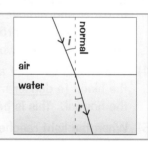
normal   i   air   water   r

Find the Refractive Index of Glass Using a Glass Block   PRACTICAL

You need to be able to describe an <u>experiment</u> to find the <u>refractive index of a glass block</u> — it's pretty much the same as the rectangular block experiment on the last page.

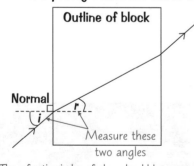
Outline of block
Normal   r   i   Measure these two angles

The refractive index of glass should be around 1.5, so if you get a ridiculous answer then you've gone wrong somewhere.

1) Draw around a <u>rectangular glass block</u> on a piece of paper and direct a <u>ray of light</u> through it at an <u>angle</u>. Trace the <u>incident</u> and <u>emergent</u> rays, remove the block, then draw in the <u>refracted ray</u> between them.

2) You then need to <u>draw in the normal</u> at <u>90°</u> to the edge of the block, at the point where the ray <u>enters</u> the block.

3) Use a <u>protractor</u> to measure the <u>angle of incidence</u> (*i*) and the <u>angle of refraction</u> (*r*), as shown. Remember — these are the angles made with the <u>normal</u>.

4) Calculate the <u>refractive index</u> (*n*) using <u>Snell's law</u>: $n = \dfrac{\sin i}{\sin r}$.

5) Et voilà — you should have found the refractive index of the block.

Revise refraction — but don't let it slow you down...

Make sure that you can scribble a decent version of the glass block diagram — if you know it, it's easy marks.

Q1   A ray of light passes into a glass block from the air. The angle of incidence is 34°. If the speed of light in the block is 1.9×10^8 m/s, calculate the angle of refraction of the ray. Use $c = 3.0 \times 10^8$ m/s.   [3 marks]

Refractive Index and Critical Angles

Still with me? Great. There's one more angle you need to learn about...

Use Semicircular Blocks to Show Total Internal Reflection | PRACTICAL

1) As you've just seen, light going from a material with a <u>higher</u> refractive index to a material with a <u>lower</u> refractive index <u>speeds up</u> and so bends <u>away from the normal</u> — e.g. when travelling from <u>glass into air</u>.

2) If you keep <u>increasing</u> the <u>angle of incidence</u> (*i*), the <u>angle of refraction</u> (*r*) gets closer and closer to <u>90°</u>.

3) Eventually *i* reaches a <u>critical angle</u> *C* for which <u>*r* = 90°</u>. The light is refracted right along the <u>boundary</u>.

4) Above this critical angle, you get <u>total internal reflection</u> — no light leaves the medium.

5) An <u>experiment</u> to demonstrate this uses a <u>semicircular block</u> instead of a rectangular one. The incident light ray is aimed at the <u>curved edge</u> of the block so that it always <u>enters at right angles</u> to the edge. This means it <u>doesn't bend</u> as it <u>enters</u> the block, only when it <u>leaves</u> from the <u>straight edge</u>.

6) To investigate the critical angle, *C*, mark the positions of the <u>rays</u> and the <u>block</u> on paper and use a <u>protractor</u> to measure *i* and *r* for <u>different angles of incidence</u>. <u>Record</u> your results in a <u>table</u>.

IF THE ANGLE OF INCIDENCE (*i*) IS...

Remember — the angle of incidence and the angle of reflection are equal, and always measured from the normal.

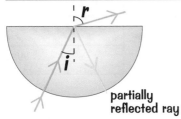

partially reflected ray

...LESS than Critical Angle:
Most of the light <u>passes out</u> but a <u>little</u> bit is <u>internally reflected</u>.

Critical angle *C*

stronger reflected ray

...EQUAL to Critical Angle:
The emerging ray comes out <u>along the surface</u>. There's a lot of <u>internal reflection</u>.

total internal reflection

...GREATER than Critical Angle:
<u>No light comes out</u>. It's <u>all</u> internally reflected, i.e. <u>total internal reflection</u>.

You Can Use Snell's Law to find Critical Angles

You can find the <u>critical angle</u>, *C*, of a material using this equation:

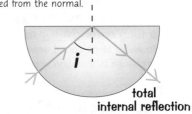

$$\sin C = \frac{1}{n}$$

n is the <u>refractive index</u> of the material.

This equation comes from Snell's law that you saw on the last page — you don't need to know how, but you do need to learn both equations.

The <u>higher the refractive index</u>, the <u>lower the critical angle</u>. For water, *C* is 49°.

Optical Fibres and Prisms Use Total Internal Reflection

1) <u>Optical fibres</u> made of <u>plastic</u> or <u>glass</u> (see p.29) consist of a <u>central core</u> surrounded by <u>cladding</u> with a <u>lower</u> refractive index.

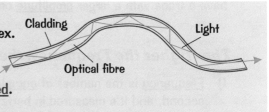

Cladding   Light

Optical fibre

2) The core of the <u>fibre</u> is so <u>narrow</u> that <u>light</u> signals passing through it <u>always</u> hit the core-cladding boundary at angles <u>higher than *C*</u> — so the light is <u>always totally internally reflected</u>. It only <u>stops working</u> if the fibre is bent <u>too sharply</u>.

1) Total internal reflection also allows us to use <u>prisms</u> to see objects that aren't in our direct line of sight. This is how a <u>periscope</u> works.

2) The ray of light travels into one prism where it is totally internally reflected by 90°.

3) It then travels to <u>another prism</u> lower down and is totally internally reflected by another 90°.

4) The ray is now travelling <u>parallel</u> to its initial path but at a <u>different height</u>.

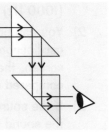

Critical angles are hard to please...

Total internal reflection only works as light tries to pass into something less dense (i.e. with a lower refractive index).

Q1 Calculate the critical angle for a material with a refractive index of 1.4. [2 marks]

Sound Waves

You hear <u>sounds</u> when <u>vibrations</u> reach your eardrums. What you hear depends on the <u>properties</u> of the <u>sound wave</u> that reaches you (as well as how much earwax you've got down your lugholes...).

Sound Travels as a Wave

1) <u>Sound waves</u> are <u>longitudinal waves</u> caused by <u>vibrating objects</u>. The vibrations are passed through the surrounding medium as a series of compressions.

2) The sound may eventually reach someone's <u>eardrum</u>, at which point the person might <u>hear it</u> — the <u>human ear</u> is capable of hearing sounds with frequencies between <u>20 Hz</u> and <u>20 000 Hz</u>.
(Although in practice some people can't hear some of the higher frequency sounds.)

3) Because sound waves are caused by <u>vibrating particles</u>, in general the <u>denser</u> the medium, the <u>faster</u> sound travels through it. This also means it <u>can't</u> travel through a <u>vacuum</u>, where there <u>aren't any particles</u>.

4) Sound generally travels <u>faster in solids</u> than in liquids, and faster in liquids than in gases.

5) Sound waves will be <u>reflected</u> by <u>hard flat surfaces</u>. Things like <u>carpets</u> and <u>curtains</u> act as <u>absorbing surfaces</u>, which will <u>absorb</u> sounds rather than reflect them.

6) <u>Sound waves</u> will also <u>refract</u> (change direction) as they enter <u>different media</u>. As they enter <u>denser</u> material, they <u>speed up</u>.
(However, since sound waves are always <u>spreading out so much</u>, the change in direction is <u>hard to spot</u> under normal circumstances.)

An Oscilloscope Can Display Sound Waves

1) A <u>sound wave receiver</u>, such as a <u>microphone</u>, can pick up sound waves travelling through the air.

2) To <u>display</u> these sound waves, and <u>measure their properties</u>, you can plug the microphone into an <u>oscilloscope</u>. The microphone <u>converts</u> the sound waves to electrical signals.

3) An <u>oscilloscope</u> is a device which can display the microphone signal as a <u>trace</u> on a screen.

4) The <u>appearance</u> of the wave on the screen tells you whether the sound is <u>loud</u> or <u>quiet</u>, and <u>high-</u> or <u>low-pitched</u>. You can even take <u>detailed measurements</u> to calculate the <u>frequency</u> of the sound (see next page) by <u>adjusting the settings</u> of the display.

Loudness Increases with Amplitude

The <u>greater the amplitude</u> of a wave, the <u>more energy</u> it carries. In <u>sound</u> this means it'll be <u>louder</u>. <u>Louder</u> sound waves will also have a trace with a larger <u>amplitude</u> on an oscilloscope.

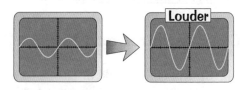

The Higher the Frequency, the Higher the Pitch

1) <u>Frequency</u> is the number of <u>complete vibrations</u> each second, and it's measured in hertz (Hz) — 1 Hz is equal to 1 vibration per second. Other common <u>units</u> are <u>kHz</u> (1000 Hz) and <u>MHz</u> (1 000 000 Hz).

2) You can <u>compare</u> the <u>frequency</u> of waves on an <u>oscilloscope</u> — the <u>more complete cycles</u> displayed on the screen, the <u>higher the frequency</u> (if the waves are being compared on the <u>same scale</u> — see the next page).

3) If the source of sound vibrates with a <u>high frequency</u> the sound is <u>high-pitched</u>, e.g. a <u>squeaking mouse</u>. If the source of sound vibrates with a <u>low frequency</u> the sound is <u>low-pitched</u>, e.g. a <u>mooing cow</u>.

4) The <u>traces</u> on the right are <u>very important</u>, so make sure you know them.

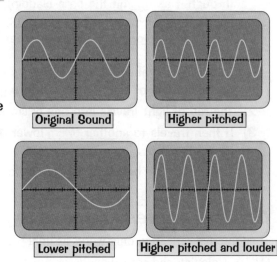

Sound Waves

All sounds have <u>pitch</u> and <u>loudness</u>. These can both be measured with a <u>microphone</u> and an <u>oscilloscope</u>.

Find the Period of a Wave on an Oscilloscope to get its Frequency

1) The <u>horizontal axis</u> on the oscilloscope display is <u>time</u>.

2) The time between <u>each division</u> on the scale can be <u>adjusted</u> to get a clear, readable trace. Here, each division has been set to show <u>0.00001 s</u>.

3) Adjust the <u>time division setting</u> until the display shows <u>at least 1 complete cycle</u>, like this.

4) Read off the <u>period</u> — the <u>time</u> taken for <u>one complete cycle</u>.

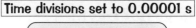
Time divisions set to 0.00001 s

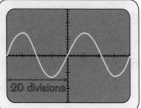
20 divisions

- Here 1 cycle crosses <u>20 divisions</u>, so <u>period</u> = 20 × 0.00001 s = <u>0.0002 s</u>.
- <u>Frequency</u> = 1 ÷ period (see p.27)
  = 1 ÷ 0.0002 s = 5000 Hz = <u>5 kHz</u>.

You Can Use an Oscilloscope to Measure the Speed of Sound

By attaching a <u>signal generator</u> to a speaker you can generate sounds with a <u>specific frequency</u>. You can use <u>two microphones</u> and an <u>oscilloscope</u> to find the <u>wavelength</u> of the sound waves generated:

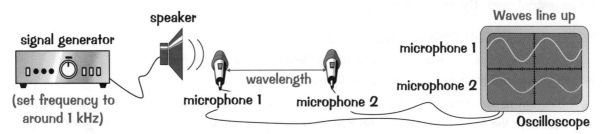

speaker

signal generator

(set frequency to around 1 kHz)

wavelength

microphone 1   microphone 2

Waves line up

microphone 1

microphone 2

Oscilloscope

1) The <u>detected waves</u> at each microphone can be seen as <u>a separate wave</u> on the oscilloscope.

2) Start with <u>both microphones</u> next to the speaker, then slowly <u>move one away</u> until the <u>two waves</u> are <u>aligned</u> on the display, but exactly <u>one wavelength apart</u>.

3) <u>Measure the distance</u> between the microphones to find the <u>wavelength</u> (λ).

4) You can then use the formula $v = f \times \lambda$ (see p. 27) to find the <u>speed</u> (v) of the <u>sound waves</u> passing through the <u>air</u> — the <u>frequency</u> (f) is whatever you set the <u>signal generator</u> to in the first place.

The two traces have the same frequency as they're detecting the same sound waves, but amplitude (loudness) is lost over distance.

The speed of sound in air is around <u>340 m/s</u>, so check your results <u>roughly agree</u> with this.

You can measure the speed of sound in other ways...

For example, you can ask a friend to stand a long distance away (e.g. 100 m) and bang a drum (or do something that makes a loud bang). You can use a stopwatch to measure the time taken between you seeing the person make the noise, and when you hear it. Then use the $v = s/t$ equation (see page 1) to work out the speed.

Q1   The density of the Earth's atmosphere decreases with altitude. A plane flying at a high altitude is heard from the ground. Describe and explain what happens to the speed of a sound wave as it travels from the plane to the ground.   [2 marks]

Q2   A signal generator connected to a speaker is used to produce sound waves at a frequency of 560 Hz. If the speed of sound is roughly 340 m/s, calculate the approximate wavelength of the sound waves.   [2 marks]

Revision Questions for Section 3

Phew, hurrah, yay — made it to the end of this section. Now it's time to get stuck into some revision questions...
- Try these questions and <u>tick off each one</u> when you <u>get it right</u>.
- When you've done <u>all the questions</u> for a topic and are <u>completely happy</u> with it, tick off the topic.

Wave Basics (p.27-28) ☑

1) Draw a diagram to illustrate frequency, wavelength and amplitude. ☑
2) What is the formula to calculate the frequency of a wave from the period? ☑
3) Find the frequency of a wave with wavelength 0.3 cm and speed 150 m/s. ☑
4) What is the main difference between a transverse wave and a longitudinal wave? ☑
5) What is the Doppler effect? ☑
6) Write down all seven types of EM radiation in order of increasing frequency
   and decreasing wavelength. ☑
7) Write down all the colours of visible light in order of increasing frequency and decreasing wavelength. ☑

Electromagnetic Waves (p.29-31) ☑

8) Describe one common use of each of the seven types of EM waves. ☑
9) Which is generally more hazardous — low frequency or high frequency EM radiation? ☑
10) Describe the harmful effects on the human body that can be caused by
    microwaves, infrared, UV and gamma rays. ☑

Reflection and Refraction (p.32-35) ☑

11) A ray of light hits the surface of a mirror at an incident angle of 10° to the normal.
    What is the angle of reflection for the ray of light? ☑
12) Draw a diagram to show the path of a ray of light that travels from air, enters a rectangular block of
    glass, then exits the block back into air on the other side (use an angle of incidence larger than 0°). ☑
13) a) Write down Snell's law.
    b) A beam of light travelling through air enters a material with $i = 30°$.
       It refracts so that $r = 20°$. What is the refractive index of the material? ☑
14) In which of the cases A to D below would the ray of light be totally internally reflected?
    (The critical angle for glass is approximately 42°.) ☑

(A) air	(B) glass	(C) air	(D) air
glass	air	50° glass	40° glass
50°	50°		

15) Give one practical use of total internal reflection. ☑

Sound Waves (p.36-37) ☑

16) True or false? Sound waves are longitudinal waves. ☑
17) This is a diagram of a sound wave displayed on an oscilloscope. ⟶
    a) What is happening to the loudness of the sound?
    b) What is happening to the pitch of the sound? ☑
18) Explain how you would find the frequency of a wave from an oscilloscope display. ☑
19) Describe an experiment to measure the speed of sound in air. ☑

Conservation of Energy

I hope you're feeling lively — this module is all about <u>energy</u>. The main thing to always remember about energy is that you can never make it or lose it — you just <u>transfer it</u> from one store to another.

Energy is Transferred Between Energy Stores

<u>Energy</u> can be held in different <u>stores</u>. Here are the stores you need to learn, plus examples of <u>objects</u> with energy in each of <u>these stores</u>:

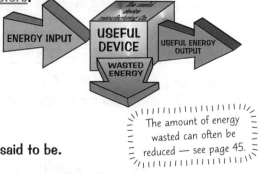

1) <u>KINETIC</u>.............................. — anything <u>moving</u> has energy in its <u>kinetic energy store</u>.
2) <u>THERMAL</u>............................. — <u>any object</u> — the <u>hotter</u> it is, the <u>more</u> energy it has in this <u>store</u>.
3) <u>CHEMICAL</u> .... — anything that can release energy by a <u>chemical reaction</u>, e.g. <u>food</u>, <u>fuels</u>.
4) <u>GRAVITATIONAL POTENTIAL</u>... — anything in a <u>gravitational field</u> (i.e. anything which can <u>fall</u>).
5) <u>ELASTIC POTENTIAL</u>.............. — anything stretched, like <u>springs</u> and <u>rubber bands</u>.
6) <u>ELECTROSTATIC</u>................... — e.g. two <u>charges</u> that attract or repel each other.
7) <u>MAGNETIC</u> .... — e.g. two <u>magnets</u> that attract or repel each other.
8) <u>NUCLEAR</u>........................... — <u>atomic nuclei</u> release energy from this store in <u>nuclear reactions</u>.

Energy can be <u>transferred between stores</u> in <u>four</u> main ways:

<u>Mechanically</u> — an object moving due to a <u>force</u> acting on it, e.g. pushing, pulling, stretching or squashing.
<u>Electrically</u> — a charge moving through a <u>potential difference</u>, e.g. charges moving round a circuit.
<u>By heating</u> — energy transferred from a <u>hotter</u> object to a <u>colder</u> object, e.g. heating a pan of water on a hob.
<u>By radiation</u> — energy transferred e.g. by light/sound <u>waves</u>, e.g. energy from the Sun reaching Earth as light.

There is a Principle of Conservation of Energy

There are plenty of different <u>stores</u> of energy, but <u>energy always obeys the principle below</u>:

> <u>Energy</u> can be <u>stored</u>, <u>transferred</u> between stores, and <u>dissipated</u> — but it can never be <u>created or destroyed</u>. The <u>total energy</u> of a <u>closed system</u> has <u>no net change</u>.

> Dissipated is a fancy way of saying the energy is spread out and lost.

A <u>closed system</u> is just a system (a collection of objects) that can be treated completely on its own, <u>without any matter</u> being exchanged with the <u>surroundings</u>.

Most Energy Transfers Involve Some Losses, Often by Heating

1) Another <u>important principle</u> you need to know is:

> Energy is <u>only useful</u> when it is <u>transferred</u> from one store to a <u>useful store</u>.

2) <u>Useful devices</u> can <u>transfer energy</u> from <u>one store</u> to a <u>useful store</u>.

3) However, some of the <u>input energy</u> is always <u>lost or wasted</u>, often to <u>thermal energy stores</u> by <u>heating</u>. For example, a <u>motor</u> will transfer energy to its <u>kinetic energy store</u> (<u>useful</u>), but will also transfer energy to the <u>thermal energy stores</u> of the motor and the surroundings (<u>wasted</u>).

ENERGY INPUT   USEFUL DEVICE   USEFUL ENERGY OUTPUT   WASTED ENERGY

4) The law of conservation of energy means that:
   <u>total energy input = useful energy output + wasted energy</u>.

5) The <u>less energy</u> that's <u>wasted</u>, the <u>more efficient</u> the device is said to be.

> The amount of energy wasted can often be reduced — see page 45.

Energy can't be created or destroyed — only talked about a lot...

This is important, so remember it. Energy can only be transferred to a different store, never destroyed.

Q1   Give the four main ways that energy can be transferred.   [1 mark]

Efficiency

So energy is <u>transferred</u> between different <u>stores</u>. But not all of the energy is transferred to <u>useful</u> stores.

You can Calculate the Efficiency of an Energy Transfer

The <u>efficiency</u> of any device is defined as:

$$\text{efficiency} = \frac{\text{useful energy output}}{\text{total energy output}} \times 100\%$$

The total energy <u>output</u> will be the same as the total energy <u>input</u>, because of the principle of conservation of energy (see p.39).

You should give efficiency as a <u>percentage</u>, i.e. <u>75%</u>.

All devices have an efficiency, but because some energy is <u>always wasted</u>, the efficiency <u>can never be</u> equal to or higher than <u>100%</u>.

How to Use the Formula — Nothing to It

1) You find how much energy is <u>supplied</u> to a machine — the <u>total</u> energy <u>INPUT</u>. This equals the <u>total</u> energy <u>OUTPUT</u>.

2) You find how much <u>useful energy</u> the machine <u>delivers</u> — the <u>useful</u> energy <u>OUTPUT</u>. An exam question either tells you this directly or tells you how much is <u>wasted</u>.

3) Either way, you get those <u>two important numbers</u> and then just <u>divide</u> the <u>smaller one</u> by the <u>bigger one</u>, then multiply by 100, to get a value for <u>efficiency</u> somewhere between <u>0 and 100%</u>. Easy.

> **Example:** A toaster transfers 216 000 J of energy electrically from the mains. 84 000 J of energy is transferred to the bread's thermal energy store. Calculate the efficiency of the toaster.
>
> $$\text{efficiency} = \frac{\text{useful energy output}}{\text{total energy output}} \times 100\%$$
>
> $$= \frac{84\,000}{216\,000} \times 100 = 38.888... = \underline{39\%} \text{ (to 2 s.f.)}$$

4) The other way they might ask it is to tell you the <u>efficiency</u> and the <u>total energy output</u> and ask for the <u>useful energy output</u>, or they could tell you the <u>efficiency</u> and <u>useful energy output</u> and ask for the <u>total energy output</u>. You need to be able to swap the formula round.

We Generally Can't Do Anything Useful with Wasted Energy

1) <u>The wasted energy</u> that's <u>output</u> by a device is transferred to less useful stores — normally by <u>heating</u>, or by <u>light</u> or <u>sound</u>. As the energy is <u>transferred</u> away from the device to its surroundings, the <u>energy</u> often spreads out and becomes <u>less concentrated</u> — we say it <u>dissipates</u>.

> For example, a <u>pan of water</u> on a <u>hob</u> — the hob will transfer energy to the water, but <u>some energy</u> will be <u>dissipated</u> to the surrounding air by heating.

2) According to the <u>principle of conservation of energy</u> (see page 39), the <u>total</u> amount of <u>energy</u> stays the <u>same</u>. So the energy is still there, but it <u>can't be easily used</u> or <u>collected back in</u> again.

Make sure your revising efficiency is high...

So one really important thing to take from here — devices that transfer energy from one store to other stores will always transfer energy to stores that aren't useful. And when I say always, I mean always. <u>Always</u>. (Always.)

Q1   An electrical device wastes 420 J of energy when it has an input energy of 500 J. Calculate the efficiency of the device.   [3 marks]

Energy Transfers

More! More! Tell me more about energy transfers please! OK, since you insist:

You Need to be Able to Describe Energy Transfers

In the exam, they can ask you about <u>any device</u> or <u>energy transfer system</u> they feel like. So it's no good just learning the examples here and on the next page — you need to <u>understand the patterns</u>, and analyse how energy moves between stores in different situations.

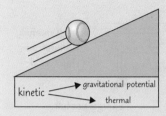

A BALL ROLLING UP A SLOPE:
Energy is transferred <u>mechanically</u> from the <u>kinetic</u> energy store of the ball to its <u>gravitational potential</u> energy store. Some energy is transferred <u>mechanically</u> to the <u>thermal</u> energy stores of the ball and the <u>slope</u> (due to <u>friction</u>), and then <u>by heating</u> to the <u>thermal</u> energy stores of the <u>surroundings</u> — this energy is <u>wasted</u>.

A BAT HITTING A BALL:
Some energy is <u>usefully transferred mechanically</u> from the <u>kinetic energy store</u> of the bat to the <u>kinetic energy store</u> of the ball. The rest of the energy is <u>wasted</u>. Some energy in the kinetic energy store of the bat is transferred <u>mechanically</u> to the <u>thermal energy stores</u> of the bat, the ball and their surroundings. The remaining energy is carried away by <u>sound</u>.

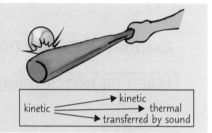

AN ELECTRIC KETTLE BOILING WATER:
Energy is transferred <u>electrically</u> from the mains to the <u>thermal energy store</u> of the kettle's <u>heating element</u>. It is then transferred <u>by heating</u> to the <u>thermal energy store</u> of the water. Some energy is <u>wasted</u>, and transferred <u>by heating</u> from the thermal energy stores of the heating element and the water to the thermal energy stores of the <u>surroundings</u>.

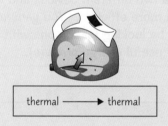

A BATTERY-POWERED TOY CAR:
Energy is usefully transferred <u>electrically</u> from the <u>chemical energy store</u> of the battery to the <u>kinetic energy store</u> of the car and carried away by <u>light</u> from the headlights. <u>Wasteful</u> energy transfers also occur, to <u>thermal energy stores</u> of the car and surroundings, and wastefully carried away by <u>sound</u>.

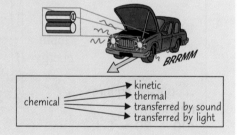

A BUNSEN BURNER AND BEAKER:
Energy is usefully transferred <u>by heating</u> from the <u>chemical energy store</u> of the gas to the <u>thermal energy stores</u> of the beaker and the water. Energy is also <u>wastefully</u> transferred by heating to the <u>thermal energy stores</u> of the stand and the surroundings. Some energy is also carried away by <u>light</u>.

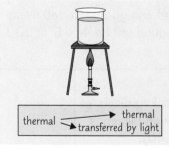

Revise this — it won't be wasted energy...
Energy stores pop up everywhere in physics, the pesky scoundrels — make sure you've got to grips with them.

Q1 Describe the energy transfers for a falling ball landing on the ground without bouncing. [3 marks]

Q2 Describe the energy transfers that occur when a piece of wood is burning. [2 marks]

Sankey Diagrams

This is another opportunity for a MATHS question. Fantastic.
So best prepare yourself — here's what those <u>Sankey diagrams</u> are all about...

The Thickness of the Arrow Represents the Amount of Energy

The idea of <u>Sankey (energy transformation) diagrams</u> is to make it <u>easy to see</u> at a glance how much of the <u>input energy</u> is being <u>usefully employed</u> compared with how much is being <u>wasted</u>.

The <u>thicker the arrow</u>, the <u>more energy</u> it represents
— so you see a big <u>thick arrow going in</u>, then several
<u>smaller arrows going off</u> it to show the different energy
transformations taking place.

You can have either a little <u>sketch</u> or a properly
<u>detailed diagram</u> where the width of each arrow is
proportional to the number of joules it represents.

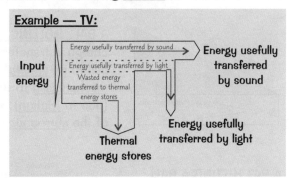

Example — TV:

Example — Sankey Diagram for a Simple Motor:

<u>HERE'S THE SKETCH VERSION:</u>

You don't know the actual amounts, but you can see that most of the energy is being wasted, and that it's mostly wasted as heat.

EXAM QUESTIONS:
With sketches, you might be asked to compare two different devices and say which is more efficient. You generally want to be looking for the one with the thickest useful energy arrow(s).

<u>AND HERE'S THE DETAILED ONE:</u>

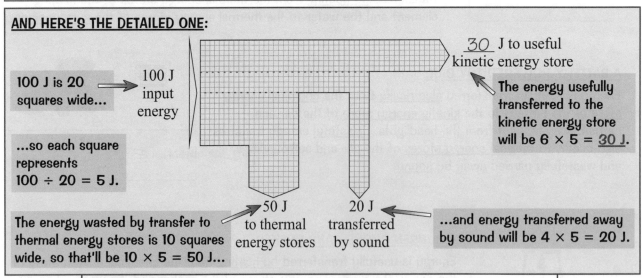

100 J is 20 squares wide...

...so each square represents 100 ÷ 20 = 5 J.

The energy wasted by transfer to thermal energy stores is 10 squares wide, so that'll be 10 × 5 = 50 J...

30 J to useful kinetic energy store

The energy usefully transferred to the kinetic energy store will be 6 × 5 = 30 J.

...and energy transferred away by sound will be 4 × 5 = 20 J.

EXAM QUESTIONS:
In an exam, the most likely question you'll get about detailed Sankey diagrams is filling in one of the numbers or calculating the efficiency. The efficiency is straightforward enough if you can work out the numbers (see p.40).

Don't waste energy — turn the TV off while you revise...

If they ask you to draw your own Sankey diagram in the exam, if they don't give you the figures, a sketch is all they'll expect. Just give a rough idea of where the energy goes. E.g. a filament lamp turns most of the input energy into heat.

Q1   Sketch the Sankey diagram of a battery-powered torch.   [2 marks]

Energy Transfer by Heating

Energy tends to be transferred away from a hotter object to its cooler surroundings.

Energy Transfer by Heating can Happen in Three Different Ways

1) Energy can be transferred by heating through radiation, conduction or convection.
2) Thermal radiation is the transfer of energy by heating by infrared electromagnetic waves (see below).
3) Conduction and convection are energy transfers that involve the transfer of energy by particles.
4) Conduction is the main form of energy transfer by heating in solids (see below).
5) Convection is the main form of energy transfer by heating in liquids and gases (see the next page).
6) Emission of thermal radiation occurs in solids, liquids and gases. Any object can both absorb and emit thermal radiation, whether or not conduction or convection are also taking place.
7) The bigger the temperature difference, the faster energy is transferred between the thermal energy stores of a body and its surroundings. Kinda makes sense.

Thermal Radiation Involves Emission of Electromagnetic Waves

Thermal radiation can also be called infrared (IR) radiation, and it consists purely of electromagnetic waves of a certain range of frequencies. It's next to visible light in the electromagnetic spectrum (see p.28).

1) All objects are continually emitting and absorbing infrared radiation.
2) An object that's hotter than its surroundings emits more radiation than it absorbs (as it cools down). And an object that's cooler than its surroundings absorbs more radiation than it emits (as it warms up).
3) You can feel this radiation if you stand near something hot like a fire.
4) Some colours and surfaces absorb and emit radiation better than others — see page 45 for more on this.

Conduction — Occurs Mainly in Solids

In a solid, the particles are held tightly together. So when one particle vibrates, it collides with other particles nearby and the vibrations quickly pass from particle to particle.

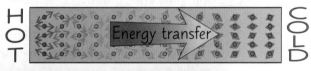

> Thermal conduction is the process where vibrating particles transfer energy from their kinetic energy store to the kinetic energy stores of neighbouring particles.

This process continues throughout the solid and gradually some of the energy is passed all the way through the solid, causing a rise in temperature at the other side of the solid. It's then usually transferred to the thermal energy stores of the surroundings (or anything else touching the object).

You Can do an Experiment to Demonstrate Conduction

PRACTICAL

1) Attach beads at regular intervals (e.g. every 5 cm) to one half of a long (at least 30 cm) metal bar using wax.
2) Hold the metal bar in a clamp stand, and, using a Bunsen burner, heat the side of the bar with no beads attached from the very end.
3) As time goes on, energy is transferred along the bar by conduction and the temperature increases along the rod.
4) The wax holding the beads in place will gradually melt and the beads will fall as the temperature increases, starting with the bead closest to the point of heating. This illustrates conduction.

Transferring heat between bodies — not as much fun as it sounds...

Of the three energy transfer methods on this page, radiation is the only one that works through a vacuum, as it doesn't rely on there being any particles about. And that's how we can get heat from the Sun across the vacuum of space.

Q1   Name the main form of energy transfer by heating in a solid.   [1 mark]

Convection

Gases and liquids are usually free to slosh about — and that allows them to transfer energy by convection, which is a much more effective process than conduction.

Convection of Heat — Liquids and Gases Only

> Convection occurs when the more energetic particles move from the hotter region to the cooler region — and transfer energy as they do.

This is how immersion heaters in kettles and hot water tanks and (unsurprisingly) convector heaters work. Convection simply can't happen in solids because the particles can't move (apart from vibrating, see page 54).

The Immersion Heater Example

In a bit more detail:

1) Energy is transferred from the heater coils to the thermal energy store of the water by conduction (particle collisions).

2) The particles near the coils get more energy, so they start moving around faster. This means there's more distance between them, i.e. the water expands and becomes less dense.

3) This reduction in density means that hotter water tends to rise above the denser, cooler water.

4) As the hot water rises it displaces (moves) the colder water out of the way, making it sink towards the heater coils.

5) This cold water is then heated by the coils and rises — and so it goes on. You end up with convection currents going up, round and down, circulating the energy through the water.

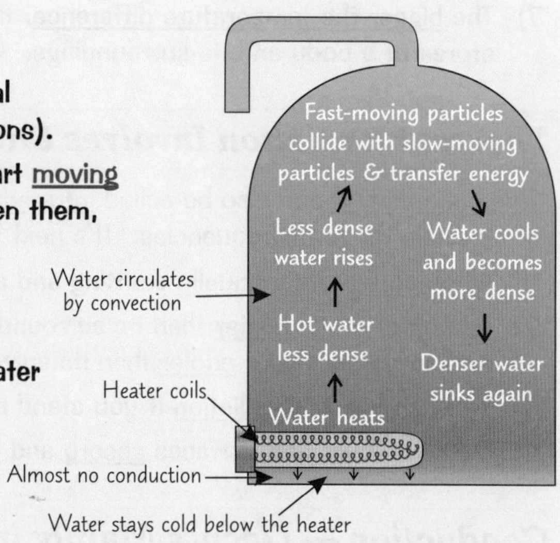

Diagram labels: Fast-moving particles collide with slow-moving particles & transfer energy. Less dense water rises. Water cools and becomes more dense. Water circulates by convection. Hot water less dense. Denser water sinks again. Heater coils. Water heats. Almost no conduction. Water stays cold below the heater.

Note that convection is most efficient in roundish or squarish containers, because they allow the convection currents to work best. Shallow, wide containers or tall, thin ones just don't work quite so well.

Also note that because the hot water rises (because of the lower density) you only get convection currents in the water above the heater. The water below it stays cold because there's almost no conduction.

> CONVECTION CURRENTS are all about CHANGES IN DENSITY. Remember that.

You Can See Convection Currents Using Coloured Crystals

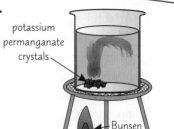

PRACTICAL

1) Place some purple potassium permanganate crystals in a beaker of cold water. Aim to put the crystals to one side of the beaker.

2) Using a Bunsen burner, gently heat the side of the beaker with the crystals at the bottom.

3) As the temperature of the water around the potassium permanganate crystals increases, they begin to dissolve, forming a bright purple solution.

4) This purple solution is carried through the water by convection, and so traces out the path of the convection currents in the beaker.

Diagram labels: potassium permanganate crystals. Bunsen burner.

You've got to love that experiment with the purple crystals...

Radiators rely on convection currents to heat a room. The radiator heats the air around it, causing it to rise, and cooler air from elsewhere in the room flows in to fill the gap, where it is then heated by the radiator, and so on and so on.

Q1 Why does hot fluid rise in a convection current? [1 mark]

More Energy Transfers by Heating

Energy transfer's great... unless you're the one losing energy. But never fear, there are things you can do to reduce the energy transferred away by radiation, convection and conduction.

You Can Reduce the Rate of Energy Transfer

1) All objects have a thermal conductivity — it describes how well an object transfers energy by conduction. Materials with a high thermal conductivity transfer energy between their particles quickly.

2) So, to reduce energy transfers away from a system by conduction, use materials with low thermal conductivity.

3) To reduce convection, you need to stop the fluid moving, and prevent convection currents from forming.

4) Insulation uses both of these techniques to reduce energy transfers.

5) Insulation such as clothes, blankets and foam cavity wall insulation all work by trapping pockets of air. The air can't move so the energy has to conduct very slowly through the pockets of air, as well as the material in between, both of which have a low thermal conductivity.

6) Some colours and surfaces will absorb and emit IR radiation better than others. For example, a black surface is better at absorbing and emitting radiation than a white one, and a matt (dull) surface is better at absorbing and emitting radiation than a shiny one.

7) So to reduce the energy transfers away from an object by thermal radiation, the object should be designed with a surface that is a poor emitter (e.g. shiny and white).

You Can Investigate Emission of Thermal Radiation With a Leslie Cube

A Leslie cube is a hollow, watertight, metal cube made of e.g. aluminium, whose four vertical faces have different surfaces (for example, matt black paint, matt white paint, shiny metal and dull metal). You can use them to investigate infrared (IR) emission by different surfaces:

matt black paint   matt white paint

1) Place an empty Leslie cube on a heat-proof mat.

2) Boil water in a kettle and fill the Leslie cube with boiling water.

PRACTICAL

3) Wait a while for the cube to warm up, then hold a thermometer against each of the four vertical faces of the cube. You should find that all four faces are the same temperature.

4) Hold an infrared detector a set distance (e.g. 10 cm) away from one of the cube's vertical faces, and record the amount of IR radiation it detects.

Leslie cube   fixed distance

5) Repeat this measurement for each of the cube's vertical faces. Make sure you position the detector at the same distance from the cube each time.

infrared detector

heat-proof mat

6) You should find that you detect more infrared radiation from the black surface than the white one, and more from the matt surfaces than the shiny ones.

7) As always, you should do the experiment more than once, to make sure your results are repeatable (p.81).

8) It's important to be careful when you're doing this experiment. Don't try to move the cube when it's full of boiling water — you might burn your hands. And be careful if you're carrying a full kettle — your mate won't thank you if you spill boiling water into their bag (or down their back).

You can also investigate how absorption depends on surface. One way is to stick ball bearings to the back of two different surfaces with wax and see which one falls off first when the surfaces are placed equal distances from a bunsen burner.

Bundle your brew in newspaper to stop it going cold...

Have a go at naming as many methods for reducing energy transfers as you can, then try this question.

Q1   Why would hot water in a black mug cool down faster than if the mug was white?   [2 marks]

Work and Power

Whenever I think of <u>power</u>, I have to stop myself from plotting world domination whilst stroking a cat.

'Work Done' is Just 'Energy Transferred'

When a <u>force</u> moves an object through a <u>distance</u>,
<u>WORK IS DONE</u> on the object and <u>ENERGY IS TRANSFERRED</u>.

1) To make something <u>move</u>, some sort of <u>force</u> needs to act on it. The thing <u>applying the force</u> needs a <u>source</u> of <u>energy</u> (like <u>fuel</u> or <u>food</u>).

2) The force does '<u>work</u>' to <u>move</u> the object and <u>energy</u> is <u>transferred mechanically</u> from one <u>store</u> to another (p.39).

3) Whether energy is transferred '<u>usefully</u>' (e.g. <u>lifting a load</u>) or is '<u>wasted</u>' (p.39), you can still say that '<u>work is done</u>'. Just like Batman and Bruce Wayne, '<u>work done</u>' and '<u>energy transferred</u>' are indeed '<u>one and the same</u>'.

When you push something along a <u>rough surface</u> (like a <u>carpet</u>) you are doing work <u>against frictional forces</u>. Energy is being <u>transferred</u> to the <u>kinetic energy store</u> of the <u>object</u> because it starts <u>moving</u>, but some is also being transferred to <u>thermal energy stores</u> due to the friction. This causes the overall <u>temperature</u> of the object to <u>increase</u>. (Like <u>rubbing your hands together</u> to warm them up.)

And Another Formula to Learn...

This formula only works if the force is in exactly the same direction as the movement.

FORCE

Distance

Work done = Force × Distance moved

$$\frac{W}{F \times d}$$

Whether the force is <u>friction</u> or <u>weight</u> or <u>tension in a rope</u>, it's the same equation. To find how much <u>work</u> has been <u>done</u> (in joules), you just multiply the <u>force in newtons</u> by the <u>distance moved in metres</u>. Easy as that. I'll show you...

Example: Some hooligan kids drag an old tractor tyre 5 m over flat ground. They pull with a total force of 340 N. Find the work done.
$W = F \times d = 340 \times 5 = 1700$ J. Phew — easy peasy isn't it?

Power is the 'Rate of Doing Work' — i.e. How Much per Second

1) <u>Power</u> is a measure of <u>how quickly work</u> is being <u>done</u>. As <u>work done</u> = <u>energy transferred</u>, you can <u>define</u> power like this:

<u>Power</u> is the <u>rate</u> at which <u>energy is transferred</u>.

2) So, the power of a <u>machine</u> is the <u>rate</u> at which it <u>transfers energy</u>. For example, if an <u>electric drill</u> has a power of <u>700 W</u>, this means it can transfer <u>700 J</u> of energy <u>every second</u>.

3) This is the <u>very easy formula</u> for power:

4) The proper unit of power is the <u>watt</u> (<u>W</u>). <u>1 W = 1 J</u> of energy <u>transferred per second</u> (J/s).

$$\text{Power} = \frac{\text{Work done}}{\text{Time taken}}$$

$$\frac{W}{P \times t}$$

Example: A motor transfers 4.8 kJ of useful energy in 2 minutes. Find its power output.
$P = W / t = 4800/120 = 40$ W (or 40 J/s)
(Note that the kJ had to be turned into J, and the minutes into seconds.)

1 kJ = 1000 J

MOTOR

4.8 kJ of useful energy transferred in 2 minutes

You've got the power — but watt to do with it...

Make sure you're happy using the equations on this page before you move on.

Q1   An appliance transfers 6 kJ of energy in 30 seconds. Calculate its power.   [2 marks]

Kinetic and Potential Energy Stores

Now you've got your head around <u>energy stores</u>, it's time to see how you can calculate the amount of energy in <u>two</u> of the most common ones — <u>kinetic</u> and <u>gravitational potential</u> energy stores.

Movement Means Energy in an Object's Kinetic Energy Store

1) Anything that is <u>moving</u> has energy in its <u>kinetic energy store</u>. Energy is transferred <u>to</u> this store when an object <u>speeds up</u> and is transferred <u>away</u> from this store when an object <u>slows down</u>.

2) The energy in the <u>kinetic energy store</u> depends on the object's <u>mass</u> and <u>speed</u>. The <u>greater its mass</u> and the <u>faster</u> it's going, the <u>more energy</u> there will be in its kinetic energy store.

3) There's a <u>slightly tricky</u> formula for it, so you have to concentrate <u>a little bit harder</u> for this one.

> Energy in kinetic energy store = ½ × mass × (speed)²

> **Example:** A car of mass 2450 kg is travelling at 38 m/s. Calculate its kinetic energy.
> $KE = \frac{1}{2}mv^2 = \frac{1}{2} \times 2450 \times 38^2 = 1\,768\,900\ J$

Raised Objects Store Energy in Gravitational Potential Energy Stores

1) <u>Lifting</u> an object in a <u>gravitational field</u> requires <u>work</u>. This causes a <u>transfer of energy</u> to the <u>gravitational potential</u> energy (g.p.e.) store of the raised object. The <u>higher</u> the object is lifted, the <u>more</u> energy is transferred to this store.

2) The amount of energy in a g.p.e. store depends on the object's <u>mass</u>, its <u>height</u> and the <u>strength</u> of the gravitational field the object is in (p.3).

> Energy in gravitational potential energy store = mass × gravitational field strength × height

3) You can use this equation to find the <u>change in energy</u> in an object's gravitational potential energy store for a <u>change in height</u>, <u>h</u>.

Falling Objects Also Transfer Energy

1) When something <u>falls</u>, energy from its <u>gravitational potential energy store</u> is transferred to its <u>kinetic energy store</u>.

2) For a falling object when there's <u>no air resistance</u>:

> Energy lost from the g.p.e. store = Energy gained in the kinetic energy store

3) It's all to do with the Principle of the Conservation of Energy — see page 39.

4) In real life, <u>air resistance</u> (p.4) acts against all falling objects — it causes some energy to be transferred to <u>other energy stores</u>, e.g. the <u>thermal</u> energy stores of the <u>object</u> and <u>surroundings</u>.

Make the most of your potential — jump on your bed...

Wow, that's a lot of energy equations. Make sure you know how to use them all, and remember that the energy in an object's kinetic energy store only changes if it's changing its speed. Now have a crack at this delightful question...

Q1   A 2.0 kg object is dropped from a height of 10 m. Calculate the speed of the object after it has fallen 5.0 m, assuming there is no air resistance. *g* = 10 N/kg. [5 marks]

Non-Renewable Energy and Power Stations

There are different types of energy resources. They fit into two broad types: renewable and non-renewable.

Non-Renewable Energy Resources Will Run Out One Day

The non-renewables are the three FOSSIL FUELS and NUCLEAR:

1) Coal
2) Oil
3) Natural gas
4) Nuclear fuels (e.g. uranium and plutonium), see p.49.

a) They will all 'run out' one day.
b) They all do damage to the environment.
c) But they provide most of our energy.

Most Power Stations Use Steam to Drive a Turbine

Most electricity we use is generated from the four NON-RENEWABLE sources of energy (coal, oil, natural gas and nuclear) in big power stations, which are all pretty much the same apart from the boiler (see p.49). Learn the basic features of the typical power station shown here and the energy transfers involved.

1) As the fossil fuel burns (in oxygen) the energy in its chemical energy store is transferred to the thermal energy store of the water by heating.

2) The water boils to form steam, which turns a turbine, transferring energy mechanically to the kinetic energy store of the turbine.

3) As the turbine revolves, so does the generator, which produces an electric current (see page 63). The generator transfers the energy electrically away from the power station, via the national grid.

Boiler | steam | Turbine | Generator | Grid
Fuel
Chemical energy store → Thermal energy store → water → Kinetic energy store → Kinetic energy store → Transferred away electrically

Fossil Fuels are Linked to Environmental Problems

Burning fossil fuels (oil, natural gas and coal) causes a lot of problems, mainly environmental. But at the moment we still rely on them the most to provide the energy needed to generate electricity.

ADVANTAGES:

1) Burning fossil fuels releases a lot of energy, relatively cheaply.
2) Energy from fossil fuels doesn't rely on the weather, like a lot of renewable energy (see pages 49-51), so it's a reliable energy source.
3) We have lots of fossil fuel power stations already, so we don't need to spend money on new technology to use them.

DISADVANTAGES:

1) All three fossil fuels release carbon dioxide (CO_2) into the atmosphere when burned in power stations. All this CO_2 contributes to global warming and climate change.
2) Burning coal and oil also releases sulfur dioxide (SO_2), which causes acid rain. Acid rain can harm trees and soils and can have a huge impact on wildlife.
3) And a massive disadvantage of using fossil fuels is that THEY'RE EVENTUALLY GOING TO RUN OUT.

Fossil fuels — a coal lotta trouble...

Using fossil fuels can be messy too — "opencast" coal mining leaves loads of soot and sludge all over the landscape, and oil spills can cause serious environmental problems, affecting the wildlife that lives in and around the sea. Not good. But they currently provide most of our energy, so we don't have much choice...

Q1 Describe how a coal-fired power station works. [2 marks]

Section 4 — Energy Resources and Energy Transfer

Nuclear, Wind and Geothermal Power

Well, who'd have thought... there's energy lurking about inside atoms, on the breeze and deep underground.

Nuclear Reactors are Just Fancy Boilers

1) A nuclear power station is mostly the same as the one on p. 48.
The difference is that nuclear fission (p. 72), e.g. of uranium,
produces the heat to make steam to drive turbines etc.,
rather than burning. So the boiler is a bit different: ⟹

Uranium fuel rods — Steam generator — Steam to turbine — Return water

2) During the process, energy is transferred from nuclear energy stores
to thermal energy stores by heating, then mechanically to kinetic
energy stores, and finally transferred electrically through the national grid.

3) Nuclear reactors are expensive to build and maintain, and take longer to start up than fossil fuel ones.

4) Processing the uranium before you use it causes pollution, and there's always
a risk of leaks of radioactive material, or even a major catastrophe like at Chernobyl.

5) A big problem with nuclear power is the radioactive waste that you always get.

6) When they're too old and inefficient, nuclear power stations have to be decommissioned
(shut down and made safe) — that's expensive too.

7) But there are many advantages to nuclear power. It doesn't produce any of the greenhouse gases
which contribute to global warming. Also, there's still plenty of uranium left in the ground
(although it can take a lot of money and energy to make it suitable for use in a reactor).

Wind Farms — Lots of Wind Turbines

1) Wind power involves putting lots of wind turbines up in exposed places
— like on moors, around the coast or out at sea.

2) Wind turbines use energy from the kinetic energy store of moving air to
generate electricity. Wind turns the blades, which turn a generator inside it.

3) Wind turbines are quite cheap to run — they're very tough and reliable, and the wind is free.

4) Wind power doesn't produce any polluting waste and it's renewable — the wind's never going to run out.

5) But there are disadvantages. They spoil the view. You need about 1500 wind turbines to replace one
coal-fired power station and 1500 of them cover a lot of ground — which would have a big effect on the
scenery. And they can be very noisy, which can be annoying for people living nearby.

6) Another problem is that sometimes the wind isn't strong enough to generate any power. It's also
impossible to increase supply when there's extra demand (e.g. when Coronation Street starts).

7) And although the wind is free, it's expensive to set up a wind farm, especially out at sea.

Geothermal Power — Heat from Underground

1) This is only possible in certain places where hot rocks lie quite near to
the surface. The source of much of the energy is the slow decay of
various radioactive elements including uranium deep inside the Earth.

2) Water is pumped in pipes down to the hot rocks and forced back
up due to pressure to turn a turbine which drives a generator.
So the energy is transferred from thermal energy stores to
kinetic energy stores and used to generate electricity.

national grid — turbine — generator — cold water pumped down — steam pumped up — 7 km — hot rocks

3) In some places, geothermal energy is used to heat buildings directly.

4) This is actually brilliant, free, renewable energy with no real environmental problems.

5) The main drawback is the cost of drilling down several km.

6) The cost of building a power plant is often high compared to the amount of energy we can get out of it.

7) So there are very few places where this seems to be an economic option (for now).

Paper 2

Solar and Wave Power

Sunshine and waves — a perfect beach holiday AND two sources of renewable energy.

You Can Capture the Sun's Energy Using Solar Cells

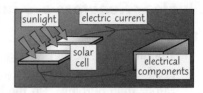

1) Solar cells (photocells) use energy from the Sun to directly generate electricity. They generate direct current (d.c.) — the same as a battery (not like the mains electricity in your home, which is a.c. (alternating current) — see p.16).

2) The Sun provides a renewable energy resource — it won't run out (not for 5 billion years anyway).

3) Solar cells are very expensive initially, but after that the energy is free and running costs are almost nil. And there's no pollution produced while using them (although some is produced during their manufacture).

4) They're usually used to generate electricity on a relatively small scale, e.g. powering individual homes.

5) It's often too expensive or not practical to connect them to the national grid — the cost of connecting them to the national grid can be enormous compared with the value of the electricity generated. Solar cells can only generate enough electricity to be useful if they have enough sunlight — which can be a problem at night (and in winter in some places). But the cells can be linked to rechargeable batteries to create a system that can store energy during the day for use at night.

6) Solar cells are often the best way to power calculators or watches that don't use much energy. They're also used in remote places where there's not much choice (e.g. deserts) and in satellites.

Solar Heating Systems — No Complex Mechanical Stuff

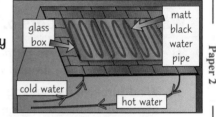

SOLAR WATER HEATING PANELS

Solar water heating panels are more simple than solar cells — they're basically just black water pipes inside a glass box. The glass lets energy from the Sun in, which is then absorbed by the black pipes and heats up the water.

Like solar cells, they cost money to set up, but are renewable and free after that. They're only used for small-scale energy production.

COOKING WITH SOLAR POWER

If you get a curved mirror, then you can focus the Sun's light. This is what happens in a solar oven. They provide a renewable energy resource for outdoor cooking. But they're slow, bulky and unreliable — they need strong sunlight to work.

All the radiation that lands on the curved mirror is focused right on your pan.

Wave Power — Lots of Little Wave Converters

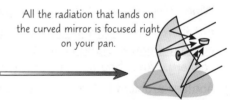

1) One way of harvesting wave power is with lots of small wave converters located around the coast. As waves come in to the shore they provide an up and down motion which can be used to drive a generator.

2) The energy is transferred from the kinetic energy store of the waves to the kinetic energy store of the turbine, and used to generate electricity.

3) There's no pollution and it's renewable.

4) The main problems are spoiling the view and being a hazard to boats.

5) It's fairly unreliable, since waves tend to die out when the wind drops.

6) Initial costs are high but there are no fuel costs and minimal running costs. Wave power is unlikely to provide energy on a large scale but it can be very useful on small islands.

Learn about wave power — and bid your cares goodbye...

Two great small-scale renewable energy resources here — they're both dependent on the weather though.

Q1   Give one negative impact of generating electricity using wind turbines.   [1 mark]

Q2   Give one advantage and one disadvantage of generating electricity using solar power.   [2 marks]

Paper 2

Generating Electricity Using Water

Water, water, everywhere. Perfect for generating electricity.

Tidal Barrages Generate Energy When the Tide Goes In and Out

1) Tidal barrages are big dams built across river estuaries, with turbines in them. As the tide comes in it fills up the estuary to a height of several metres. This water can then be allowed out through turbines at a controlled speed. It also drives the turbines on the way in.

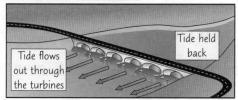

2) The energy is transferred from the kinetic energy stores of the water to the kinetic energy store of the turbine, and used to generate electricity.

3) There's no pollution and it's renewable. The main problems are preventing free access by boats, spoiling the view and altering the habitat of the wildlife.

4) Tides are pretty reliable, but the height of the tide is variable so lower tides will provide less energy than higher ones.

5) Initial costs are moderately high, but there's no fuel costs and minimal running costs.

Hydroelectricity — Catching Rainwater

1) Hydroelectric power often requires the flooding of a valley by building a big dam. Rainwater is caught and allowed out through turbines, transferring energy from the gravitational potential energy store of the water to kinetic energy stores as it falls, which is used to generate electricity.

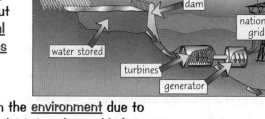

2) It's a renewable energy resource.

3) There is no pollution (as such), but there's a big impact on the environment due to flooding the valley (rotting vegetation releases methane and CO_2) and possible loss of habitat for some species. The reservoirs can also look very unsightly when they dry up. Location in remote valleys can avoid some of these problems.

4) A big advantage is immediate response to increased demand. If more energy is needed than the national grid can supply, the water's released. There's no problem with reliability except in times of drought.

5) Initial costs are high, but there's no fuel and low running costs.

Pumped Storage Gives Extra Supply Just When it's Needed

1) Most large power stations have huge boilers which have to be kept running all night even though demand is very low. This means there's a surplus of electricity at night — and it's surprisingly difficult to find a way of keeping this spare energy for later use. Pumped storage is one of the best solutions.

2) In pumped storage, 'spare' night-time electricity is used to pump water up to a higher reservoir.

3) This can then be released quickly during periods of peak demand, such as at teatime each evening, to supplement the steady delivery from the big power stations.

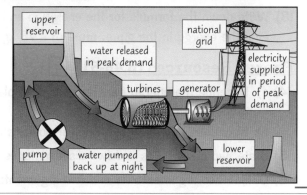

4) The 'spare' electricity is used to transfer energy back to the water's gravitational potential energy stores, so that it may generate more electricity when it is needed by flowing through the dam.

The hydroelectric power you're supplying — it's electrifying...

Some other parts of the world rely heavily on hydroelectric power for their electricity. For example, in the last few years, 99% of Norway's energy came from hydroelectric power. 99% — that's huge!

Q1   Give one advantage and one disadvantage of producing hydroelectricity.   [2 marks]

Section 4 — Energy Resources and Energy Transfer

Revision Questions for Section 4

Phew... what a relief, you've made it to the end of yet another nice long section. This one's been fairly straightforward but there are a shedload of facts to remember and you need to know the lot of them. And the best way to check that you know them all is...

• Try these questions and tick off each one when you get it right.
• When you've done all the questions for a topic and are completely happy with it, tick off the topic.

Energy Transfers and Efficiency (p.39-42) ☐

1) Name eight types of energy store.
2) State the principle of the conservation of energy.
3) What is the efficiency of a motor that has an input energy transfer of 120 J and transfers 90 J usefully to the motor's kinetic energy store?
4) Describe the energy transfers that occur in a battery-powered toy car.
5) The following Sankey diagram shows how energy is converted in a catapult.

100 J input energy transfer → kinetic energy store / thermal energy stores

   a) How much energy is converted into kinetic energy?
   b) How much energy is wasted?
   c) What is the efficiency of the catapult?

Energy Transfers by Heating (p.43-45) ☐

6) Describe the three ways that energy can be transferred by heating.
7) Describe how the energy is transferred from a heating element throughout the water in a kettle. What is this process called?
8) Describe how insulation reduces energy transfers.

Calculating Energy and Power (p.46-47) ☐

9) What's the formula for work done? A dog drags a big branch 12 m over the next-door neighbour's front lawn, pulling with a force of 535 N. How much work was done?
10) An electric motor uses 540 kJ of electrical energy in 4.5 minutes. What is its power consumption?
11) Write down the formula for the energy in an object's kinetic energy store. Find the energy in the kinetic energy store of a 78 kg sheep moving at 2.3 m/s.
12) What happens to the amount of energy in an object's gravitational potential energy store when it is lifted above the ground?
13) Write down the formula for the energy in an object's gravitational potential energy store. Find the energy in the g.p.e. store of a 78 kg sheep on top of a 2 m ladder (use $g = 10$ m/s^2).

Energy Resources (p.48-51) ☐

14) a) Describe the energy transfers that take place when burning fossil fuels to generate electricity in a typical power station.
    b) How does this differ in a nuclear power station?
15) State two advantages and two disadvantages of using fossil fuels to generate electricity.
16) Outline two arguments for and two arguments against increasing the use, in the UK, of nuclear power.
17) Describe the energy transfers that take place when the following renewable resources and methods are used to generate electricity:
    a) geothermal energy   b) waves   c) the tide
18) State one advantage and one disadvantage for each resource or method in question 17.

Density and Pressure

You might find this stuff a bit tricky — but just read it through carefully and take the pressure off.

Density is Mass per Unit Volume

The symbol for density is a Greek letter rho (ρ) — it looks like a p but it isn't.

Density is a measure of the 'compactness' (for want of a better word) of a substance. It relates the mass of a substance to how much space it takes up.

$$\text{Density } (\rho) = \frac{\text{mass } (m)}{\text{volume } (v)}$$

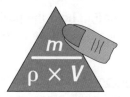

Pine $\rho = 0.5$ g/cm^3 Oil $\rho = 0.8$ g/cm^3
Water $\rho = 1$ g/cm^3
Iron $\rho = 7.9$ g/cm^3

The units of density are g/cm^3 or kg/m^3
N.B. 1 g/cm^3 = 1000 kg/m^3

1) The density of an object depends on what it's made of. Density doesn't vary with size or shape.
2) The average density of an object determines whether it floats or sinks — a solid object will float on a fluid if it has a lower density than the fluid.

You Can Find the Density of an Object from its Mass and Volume

PRACTICAL

1) To measure the density of a substance, use a balance to measure its mass.
2) If it's a box shape, start by measuring its length, width and height with an appropriate piece of equipment (e.g. a ruler). Then calculate its volume by multiplying the length, width and height together.
3) For an irregular solid, you can find its volume by submerging it in a eureka can filled with water. The water displaced by the object will be transferred to the measuring cylinder.
4) Record the volume of water in the measuring cylinder. This is also the volume of the object.
5) Plug the object's mass and volume into the formula above to find its density.

full eureka can → measuring cylinder

Pressure is Force per Unit Area

1 kPa = 1000 Pa

Pressure is a measure of the force being applied to the surface of something. It relates how much force is being applied to an object (in N) to the area that it is applied over (in m^2). Pressure is measured in pascals (Pa) or kilopascals (kPa). 1 pascal is defined as 1 N/m^2.

$$\text{Pressure} = \frac{\text{force}}{\text{area}}$$

The symbol for pressure is a p — don't confuse it with density (ρ).

1) The same force applied over a larger area creates a lower pressure.
2) In gases and liquids at rest, the pressure at any point acts equally in all directions.
3) In gases and liquids, the pressure increases with depth. The pressure is higher at the bottom of the sea than at the surface, and it is lower high up in the atmosphere than close to the Earth.

Pressure Difference in Liquids and Gases Depends on Density

Pressure difference is the difference in pressure between two points in a liquid or gas. It depends on the height difference (in m), and the density (in kg/m^3) of the substance. Gravity has an effect too — g is the gravitational field strength, which is around 10 m/s^2.

Pressure difference = height × density × gravitational field strength

Pressure — pushing down on me...

Remember — density is all about how tightly packed the particles in a substance are. Nice and simple really.

Q1 An object has a mass of 0.45 kg and a volume of 75 cm^3. Calculate its density in kg/m^3.   [3 marks]

Q2 A vase with a base area of 0.044 m^2 applies 49 N to a table surface. Calculate the pressure on the table.   [1 mark]

Changes of State

Solid ═══ melts ═══▶ Liquid ═══ boils ═══▶ Gas ═══ condenses ═══▶ Liquid ═══ solidifies ═══▶ Solid. Easy peasy.

Kinetic Theory Can Explain the Three States of Matter

1) The three states of matter are solid (e.g. ice), liquid (e.g. water) and gas (e.g. water vapour). The particles of a substance in each state are the same — only the arrangement and energy of the particles are different.

 SOLIDS — strong forces of attraction hold the particles close together in a fixed, regular arrangement. The particles don't have much energy so they can only vibrate about their fixed positions.

LIQUIDS — there are weaker forces of attraction between the particles. The particles are close together, but can move past each other, and form irregular arrangements. They have more energy than the particles in a solid — they move in random directions at low speeds.

 GASES — There are almost no forces of attraction between the particles. The particles have more energy than those in liquids and solids — they are free to move, and travel in random directions and at high speeds.

2) The energy in a substance's thermal energy store is held by its particles in their kinetic energy stores — this is what the thermal energy store actually is.

3) When you heat a liquid, the extra energy is transferred into the particles' kinetic energy stores, making them move faster. Eventually, when enough of the particles have enough energy to overcome their attraction to each other, big bubbles of gas form in the liquid — this is boiling.

> The melting point of a substance is the temperature at which it turns from a solid to a liquid. The boiling point is the temperature at which a liquid becomes a gas.

4) It's similar when you heat a solid. The extra energy makes the particles vibrate faster until eventually the forces between them are partly overcome and the particles start to move around — this is melting.

5) When a substance is melting or boiling, you're still putting in energy, but the energy's used for breaking bonds between particles rather than raising the temperature. So the substance stays at a constant temperature.

6) When a substance is condensing or freezing, bonds are forming between particles, which releases energy. This means the temperature doesn't go down until all of the substance has changed state.

Evaporation is a Special Example of Changing States

1) Evaporation is when particles escape from a liquid and become gas particles.

2) Particles can evaporate from a liquid at temperatures that are much lower than the liquid's boiling point.

3) Particles near the surface of a liquid can escape and become gas particles if:

- The particles are travelling in the right direction to escape the liquid.
- The particles are travelling fast enough (they have enough energy in their kinetic energy stores) to overcome the attractive forces of the other particles in the liquid.

4) The fastest particles (with the most energy) are most likely to evaporate from the liquid — so when they do, the average speed and energy in the kinetic energy stores of the remaining particles decreases.

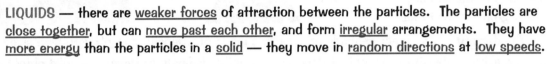

not enough energy to escape the liquid

this particle is able to escape the liquid and evaporates

not near enough the surface to escape the liquid

moving in the wrong direction to escape the liquid

5) This decrease in average particle energy means the temperature of the remaining liquid falls — the liquid cools.

6) This cooling effect can be really useful. For example, you sweat when you exercise or get hot. As the water from the sweat on your skin evaporates, it cools you down.

All this talk of kinetic theory has left me in a right state...

Unfortunately not a page about American state history. Sorry about that — it would have been a fun page (ish), but I might've got in trouble and you would've ended up snookered if any of this came up in the exam.

Q1 Explain how particles are able to escape a liquid before it reaches its boiling point. [2 marks]

Temperature and Particle Theory

Temperature-time graphs, particles in gases, and absolute zero — ooh, sounds like fun...

You Can Obtain a Temperature-Time Graph for Water | PRACTICAL

You can do a simple experiment to show that temperature remains
constant during changes of state:

1) Fill a beaker with crushed ice. Place a thermometer into the
   beaker and record the temperature of the ice.

2) Using the Bunsen burner, gradually heat the beaker full of ice.

3) Every twenty seconds, record the temperature and the current state of the ice
   (e.g. partially melted, completely melted). Continue this until the water begins to boil.

4) Plot a graph of temperature against time for your experiment.

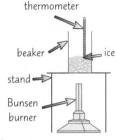

Your graph should look like this:

You get a similar one for condensing and freezing:

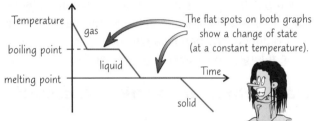

The flat spots on both graphs
show a change of state
(at a constant temperature).

Absolute Zero is as Cold as Stuff Can Get — 0 Kelvins

1) If you increase the temperature of something, you give its particles more energy — they move about more
   quickly or vibrate more. Similarly, if you cool a substance down, you reduce the energy of the particles.

2) The coldest that anything can ever get is −273 °C — this temperature is known as absolute zero.
   At absolute zero, the particles have as little energy in their kinetic stores as it's possible to get.

3) Absolute zero is the start of the Kelvin scale of temperature.

4) A temperature change of 1 °C is also a change of 1 kelvin. The two
   scales are similar — the only difference is where the zero occurs.

5) To convert from degrees Celsius to kelvins, just add 273.
   And to convert from kelvins to degrees Celsius, just subtract 273.

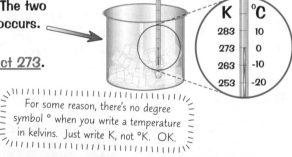

	Absolute zero	Freezing point of water	Boiling point of water
Celsius scale	−273 °C	0 °C	100 °C
Kelvin scale	0 K	273 K	373 K

For some reason, there's no degree
symbol ° when you write a temperature
in kelvins. Just write K, not °K. OK.

Energy in Particles' Kinetic Energy Stores is Proportional to Temperature

1) Particle theory says that gases consist of very small particles which are constantly moving in completely
   random directions. The particles hardly take up any space — most of the gas is empty space.

2) The particles constantly collide with and bounce off of each other and the container walls.

3) If you increase the temperature of a gas, you give its particles more energy. If you double the temperature
   (measured in kelvins), you double the average energy in the kinetic energy stores of the particles.

> The temperature of a gas (in kelvins) is proportional to
> the average energy in the kinetic energy stores of its particles.

4) As you heat up a gas, the average speed of its particles increases. Anything that's moving has energy in
   its kinetic energy store. This energy is equal to $\frac{1}{2}mv^2$, remember (see p.47).

Absolute zero — nought, zilch, not a sausage...

Nothing can be colder than zero kelvins (or −273 °C) — at this temperature, particles are pretty much still.

Q1   Find the value of 25 °C in kelvins.   [1 mark]

Particle Theory and Pressure in Gases

The pressure of a gas is explained by the movement of its particles. Fascinating stuff... Well, almost.

Particle Theory Says Colliding Gas Particles Create Pressure

1) As gas particles move about, they randomly bang into each other and whatever else gets in the way.

2) Gas particles are very light, but they sure ain't massless. When they collide with something, they exert a force on it and their momentum and direction change. In a sealed container, gas particles smash against the container's walls — creating an outward pressure.

3) This pressure depends on how fast the particles are going and how often they hit the walls.

4) If you heat a gas, the particles move faster and have more energy in their kinetic stores. This increase in energy means the particles hit the container walls harder and more frequently, resulting in a larger force, creating more pressure. In fact, temperature (in K) and pressure are proportional — double the temperature of a fixed amount of gas, and you double the pressure.

5) And if you put the same fixed amount of gas in a bigger container, the pressure will decrease, cos there'll be fewer collisions between the gas particles and the container's walls. When the volume's reduced, the particles get more squashed up and so they hit the walls more frequently, producing a larger force over a smaller surface area, which increases the pressure.

This all applies to so-called ideal gases. Ideal gases are gases that are 'well behaved', i.e. ones that this equation works for... Scientists, eh.

At Constant Temperature "pV = Constant"

Learn this equation:

For a fixed mass of gas at a constant temperature:

$$\text{pressure} \times \text{volume} = \text{constant} \implies pV = \text{constant}$$

You can also write the equation as $p_1 V_1 = p_2 V_2$

(where p_1 and V_1 are your starting conditions and p_2 and V_2 are your final conditions).
Writing it like that is much more useful a lot of the time.

EXAMPLE: A gas at a pressure of 250 kilopascals is compressed from a volume of 300 cm³ down to a volume of 175 cm³. The temperature of the gas does not change. Find the new pressure of the gas, in kilopascals.
$p_1 V_1 = p_2 V_2$ gives: $250 \times 300 = p_2 \times 175$, so $p_2 = (250 \times 300) \div 175 = $ **429 kPa (3 s.f.)**.

At Constant Volume "p/T = Constant"

Learn this equation too:

In a sealed container (i.e. constant volume):

$$\frac{\text{pressure}}{\text{temperature (in K)}} = \text{constant} \implies \frac{p}{T} = \text{constant}$$

You can also write the equation as $p_1 / T_1 = p_2 / T_2$

(where p_1 and T_1 are your starting conditions and p_2 and T_2 are your final conditions).

EXAMPLE: A container has a volume of 30 litres. It is filled with gas at a pressure of 100 kPa and a temperature of 290 K. Find the new pressure if the temperature is increased to 315 K.
$p_1/T_1 = p_2/T_2$ gives: $100 \div 290 = p_2 \div 315$ so $p_2 = 315 \times (100 \div 290) = $ **109 kPa (3 s.f.)**.

NB: The temperatures in this formula must always be in kelvins, so if they give you the temperatures in °C, convert to kelvins FIRST (by adding 273). Always keep the pressure units the same as they are in the question (in this case, kPa).

Less space, more collisions, more pressure — just like London...

The nice thing is that you don't need to fully understand the physics — you just need a bit of "common sense" about formulas. Understanding always helps of course, but you can still get the right answer without it.

Q1 An ideal gas held at a pressure of 310 kPa is compressed to a third of its original volume. Calculate the new pressure of the gas. [3 marks]

Specific Heat Capacity

The <u>temperature</u> of something <u>isn't quite the same</u> thing as the <u>energy</u> stored in the substance's thermal energy store. That's where specific heat capacity comes in...

Specific Heat Capacity Relates Temperature and Energy

1) <u>Heating</u> a substance <u>increases</u> the <u>energy</u> in its <u>thermal energy store</u>. You may see this referred to as the <u>internal energy</u> of a substance.

2) So <u>temperature</u> is a way of measuring the <u>average internal energy</u> of a substance.

3) However, it takes <u>more energy</u> to <u>increase the temperature</u> of some materials than others. E.g. you need <u>4200 J</u> to warm 1 kg of <u>water</u> by 1 °C, but only <u>139 J</u> to warm 1 kg of <u>mercury</u> by 1 °C.

4) Materials that need to <u>gain</u> lots of energy to <u>warm up</u> also <u>release</u> loads of energy when they <u>cool down</u> again. They <u>store</u> a lot of energy for a given change in temperature.

5) The <u>change in the energy</u> stored in a substance when you heat it is related to the change in its <u>temperature</u> by its <u>specific heat capacity</u>. The <u>specific heat capacity</u> of a substance is the <u>energy</u> required to change the <u>temperature</u> of an object by <u>1 °C</u> per <u>kilogram</u> of mass. E.g. water has a specific heat capacity of <u>4200 J/kg°C</u> (that's pretty high).

6) You need to know how to use the <u>equation</u> relating energy, mass, specific heat capacity and temperature.

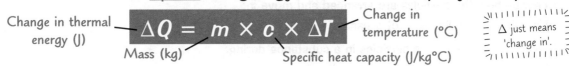

Change in thermal energy (J)

$$\Delta Q = m \times c \times \Delta T$$

Mass (kg)

Specific heat capacity (J/kg°C)

Change in temperature (°C)

Δ just means 'change in'.

You can Find the Specific Heat Capacity of Water — PRACTICAL

You can use the experiment below to find the <u>specific heat capacity</u> of <u>water</u> — or any <u>liquid</u> for that matter.

If you can, you should use a <u>thermally insulated</u> container for both of these experiments to reduce <u>energy wasted to the surroundings</u> (p.45).

You could also use a voltmeter and ammeter instead of a joulemeter. Time how long the heater was on for, then calculate the energy supplied using $E = VIt$ (p.22).

1) Use a <u>mass balance</u> to measure the <u>mass</u> of the insulating container.

2) Fill the container with <u>water</u> and measure the <u>mass</u> again. The <u>difference</u> in mass is the mass of the <u>water in the container</u>.

3) Set up the experiment as shown — make sure the joulemeter reads <u>zero</u> and place a <u>lid</u> on the container if you have one.

electric immersion heater

thermometer

joulemeter

water

to power supply

insulating container

4) Measure the <u>temperature</u> of the water, then turn on the power.

5) Keep an eye on the <u>thermometer</u>. When the temperature has increased by e.g. <u>ten degrees</u>, switch off the power and record this <u>temperature increase</u> and the <u>energy</u> on the joulemeter.

6) You can then calculate the specific heat capacity of the water by <u>rearranging</u> the equation above, and plugging in your measurements.

Your experimental value for the specific heat capacity will probably be a bit too high, since some of the heat supplied will be lost to the environment.

7) <u>Repeat</u> the whole experiment at least three times, then calculate an <u>average</u> of the specific heat capacity.

You can use a similar method to find the <u>specific heat capacity</u> of a solid. Make sure the block of material you use has two <u>holes</u> in it for the heater and thermometer, and wrap it up with an <u>insulating layer</u> before starting. When you have switched off the power and finished timing, <u>wait</u> until the temperature has <u>stopped increasing</u> before recording the <u>highest</u> final temperature — this gives the energy from the heater time to <u>spread</u> through the solid block.

I wish I had a high specific fact capacity...

Make sure you practise using that equation — it's a bit of a tricky one.

Q1 If a metal has a specific heat capacity of 420 J/kg°C, calculate how much the temperature of a 0.20 kg block of the metal will increase by if 1680 J of energy are supplied to it. [2 marks]

Paper 2

Paper 2

Revision Questions for Section 5

Lots of maths and formulae in this section. You have learnt them, haven't you? Well, there's only one way to know...

* Try these questions and <u>tick off each one</u> when you <u>get it right</u>.
* When you've done <u>all the questions</u> for a topic and are <u>completely happy</u> with it, tick off the topic.

Density and Pressure (p.53) ☐

1) What is the relationship between the density, mass and volume of a substance? ☑

2) Calculate the volume of 2 kg of water (density = 1000 kg/m³). ☑

3) How would you measure the density of an unknown cube of material in the lab? ☑

4) Draw a formula triangle containing pressure, force and area. ☐

5) What pressure does a woman weighing 600 N exert on the floor if her high-heeled shoes have an area of 5 cm² touching the floor? ☑

6) What is the formula used to work out a pressure difference in liquids and gases? ☐

Changes of State (p.54) ☑

7) Describe how the particles are arranged and move in:
   a) a solid,   b) a liquid,   c) a gas. ☑

8) Explain what happens to particles in a substance during:
   a) melting,   b) boiling,   c) evaporation. ☑

9) A substance is heated, and its temperature rises until it melts from a solid to a liquid.
   The substance then rises in temperature again until it begins to boil.
   Sketch a temperature-time graph to show this. ☑

Temperature and Pressure in Gases (p.55-56) ☑

10) What temperature is 'absolute zero' in
    a) kelvins,   b) degrees Celsius? ☑

11) How does the temperature of a gas (in kelvins) relate to the energy in the kinetic stores of its particles? ☐

12) Explain why the molecules in a gas exert a pressure on the walls of a container. ☑

13) What happens to the pressure of a gas in a sealed container if you increase the temperature? ☑

14) 500 cm³ of a fixed mass of gas at 50 kPa is forced into a 100 cm³ container.
    What is the new pressure of the gas (assuming the temperature is kept constant)? ☑

15) Another 500 cm³ of gas is kept sealed in its container at 50 kPa, but is then heated from
    a temperature of 290 K to 300 K. What is the new pressure of the gas? ☑

Specific Heat Capacity (p.57) ☑

16) What equation relates energy, mass, specific heat capacity and temperature? ☑

17) 110 J of energy is supplied to a substance to heat it from a temperature of 21 °C to 45 °C.
    The substance has a mass of 0.25 kg. Calculate the specific heat capacity of the substance. ☑

18) Describe an experiment that can be used to find the specific heat capacity of a solid. ☑

Magnets and Magnetic Fields

I think magnetism is an <u>attractive</u> subject, but don't get <u>repelled</u> by the exam — <u>revise</u>.

Magnets Produce Magnetic Fields

1) All magnets have <u>two poles</u> — north and south.

2) A <u>magnetic field</u> is a <u>region</u> where <u>magnetic materials</u> (e.g. iron) experience a <u>force</u>.

3) <u>Magnetic field lines</u> (or "lines of force") are used to show the size and direction of magnetic fields. They <u>always</u> point from <u>NORTH</u> to <u>SOUTH</u>.

4) Placing the north and south poles of <u>two</u> permanent bar magnets <u>near</u> each other creates a <u>uniform field</u> <u>between</u> the two magnets.

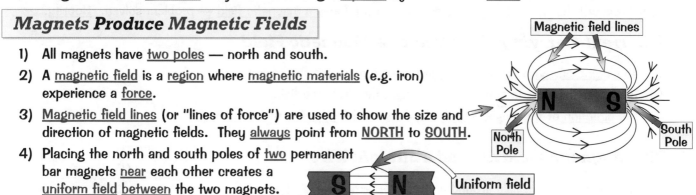

Magnetic Field Patterns can be Seen Using Compasses

PRACTICAL

1) Compasses and iron filings <u>align</u> themselves with <u>magnetic fields</u>.

2) You can use <u>multiple compasses</u> to see the magnetic field lines coming out of a bar magnet or between two bar magnets.

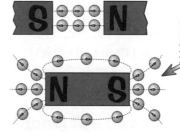

You shouldn't put the compasses too close to each other. Compasses also produce magnetic fields — you need to make sure you're measuring the field of the magnet rather than the compasses nearby.

If you don't have lots of compasses, you can just use one and move it around (trace its position on some paper before each move if it helps).

3) You could also use <u>iron filings</u> to see magnetic field patterns. Just put the magnet(s) under a piece of paper, <u>scatter</u> the iron filings on top, and <u>tap</u> the paper until the iron filings form a <u>clear pattern</u>.

Magnetism can be Induced

1) Magnets affect <u>magnetic materials</u> and other <u>magnets</u>.

2) Like poles <u>repel</u> each other and opposite poles <u>attract</u>.

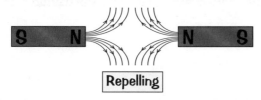
Repelling

Attracting

3) Both poles <u>attract</u> magnetic materials (that aren't magnets).

4) When magnetic materials are brought <u>near</u> to a magnet (into its <u>magnetic field</u>), that material acts as a <u>magnet</u>.

5) This magnetism has been <u>induced</u> by the original magnet.

6) The <u>closer</u> the magnet and the magnetic material get, the <u>stronger</u> the induced magnetism will be.

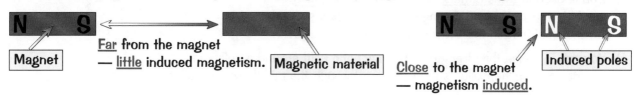

Magnet — <u>Far</u> from the magnet — <u>little</u> induced magnetism. Magnetic material — <u>Close</u> to the magnet — magnetism <u>induced</u>. Induced poles

Magnets are like farmers — surrounded by fields...

Loads of really useful things work because of magnetism — compasses, headphones, computer hard drives, MRI medical scanners, mass spectrometers, those little magnets that hold your fridge door closed...

Q1 Sketch the magnetic field pattern between two magnets that are lined up next to each other with their south poles close together. [2 marks]

Electromagnetism

Permanent magnets are great, but it would be <u>really</u> handy to be able to turn a magnetic field <u>on</u> and <u>off</u>. Well, it turns out that when <u>electric current</u> flows it <u>produces a magnetic field</u> — problem solved. <u>Hooray</u>.

A Current-Carrying Wire Creates a Magnetic Field

1) An <u>electric current</u> in a <u>conductor</u> produces a <u>magnetic field</u> around it.
2) The <u>larger</u> the electric current, the <u>stronger</u> the magnetic field.
3) The <u>direction</u> of the <u>magnetic field</u> depends on the <u>direction</u> of the <u>current</u>.

The Magnetic Field Around a Straight Wire

1) There is a magnetic field around a <u>straight, current-carrying wire</u>.
2) The field is made up of <u>concentric circles</u> with the wire in the centre.

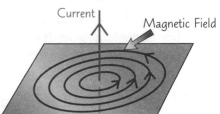

The Magnetic Field Around a Flat Circular Coil

1) The magnetic field in the <u>centre</u> of a flat circular coil of wire is similar to that of a <u>bar magnet</u>.
2) There are concentric <u>ellipses</u> (stretched circles) of magnetic field lines <u>around</u> the coil.

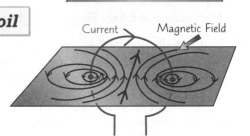

The Magnetic Field Around a Solenoid

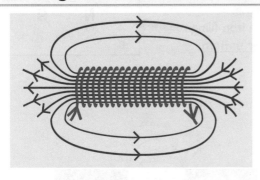

1) The magnetic field <u>inside</u> a current-carrying <u>solenoid</u> (a coil of wire) is <u>strong</u> and <u>uniform</u>.
2) <u>Outside</u> the coil, the field is just like the one around a <u>bar magnet</u>.
3) This means that the <u>ends</u> of a solenoid act like the <u>north pole</u> and <u>south pole</u> of a bar magnet. This type of magnet is called an <u>ELECTROMAGNET</u>.

Magnetic Materials can be 'Soft' or 'Hard'

1) A magnetic material is considered '<u>soft</u>' if it <u>loses</u> its induced magnetism quickly, or '<u>hard</u>' if it keeps it <u>permanently</u>.
2) <u>Iron</u> is an example of a <u>soft</u> magnetic material. <u>Steel</u> is an example of a <u>hard</u> magnetic material.
3) Iron is used in <u>transformers</u> because of this property — it needs to magnetise and demagnetise 50 times a second (mains electricity in the UK runs at 50 Hz) — see p.64.
4) You can increase the <u>strength</u> of the magnetic field around a solenoid by adding a magnetically "<u>soft</u>" <u>iron core</u> through the middle of the coil.

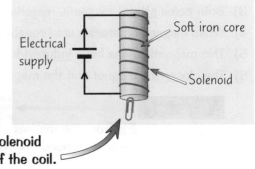

A soft iron bar walks into a solenoid...

...and suddenly has a magnetic personality. Groan. Enough of the bad jokes — electromagnetism allows us to make electric motors, doorbells, those giant magnets that pick up cars in scrapyards, magnetic locks, particle accelerators, levitating trains... Frogs can even be made to float in mid-air. Fact.

Q1   Explain the difference between 'soft' and 'hard' magnetic materials.   [2 marks]

The Motor Effect

The motor effect can happen when you put a current-carrying wire in a magnetic field. It's really useful in stuff like... well... electric motors. If you want to know exactly what it is, you'll have to keep reading.

A Current in a Magnetic Field Experiences a Force

When a current-carrying wire is put between magnetic poles, the two magnetic fields affect one another. The result is a force on the wire. This can cause the wire to move. This is called the motor effect.

This is because charged particles (e.g. electrons in a current) moving through a magnetic field will experience a force, as long as they're not moving parallel to the field lines.

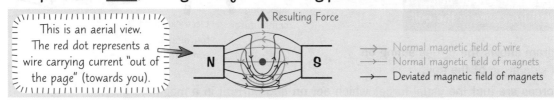

This is an aerial view. The red dot represents a wire carrying current "out of the page" (towards you).

↑ Resulting Force

→ Normal magnetic field of wire
→ Normal magnetic field of magnets
→ Deviated magnetic field of magnets

1) To experience the full force, the wire has to be at 90° to the magnetic field. If the wire runs along the magnetic field, it won't experience any force at all. At angles in between, it'll feel some force.

2) The force always acts in the same direction relative to the magnetic field of the magnets and the direction of the current in the wire.

3) A good way of showing the direction of the force is to apply a current to a set of rails inside a horseshoe magnet (shown opposite). A bar is placed on the rails, which completes the circuit. This generates a force that rolls the bar along the rails.

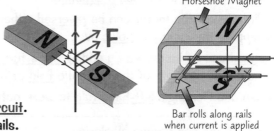

Horseshoe Magnet

Bar rolls along rails when current is applied

4) The magnitude (strength) of the force increases with the strength of the magnetic field.

5) The force also increases with the amount of current passing through the conductor.

6) Reversing the current or the magnetic field also reverses the direction of the force.

Fleming's Left-Hand Rule Tells You Which Way the Force Acts

1) They could test if you can do this, so practise it.

2) Using your left hand, point your First finger in the direction of the Field and your seCond finger in the direction of the Current.

3) Your thuMb will then point in the direction of the force (Motion).

thuMb Motion
First finger Field
seCond finger Current

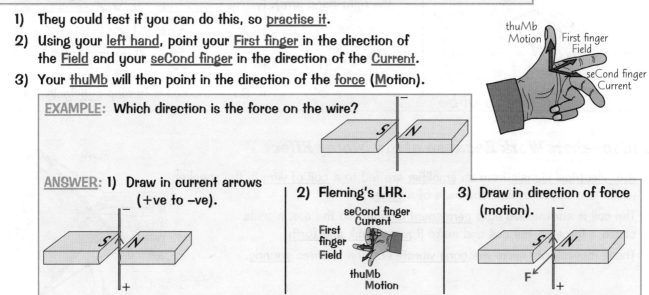

EXAMPLE: Which direction is the force on the wire?

ANSWER: 1) Draw in current arrows (+ve to −ve).

2) Fleming's LHR.
seCond finger Current
First finger Field
thuMb Motion

3) Draw in direction of force (motion).

Remember the Left-Hand Rule for the motor effect — drive on the left...

You're going to need to know the difference between left and right for this page. Learn the rule and use it — don't be scared of looking like a muppet in the exam. Learn all the details, diagrams and all, then cover the page and scribble it all down from memory. Then check back, see what you've missed, and try again.

Q1   State what the three fingers in Fleming's Left-Hand Rule represent.   [1 mark]

Paper 2
Paper 2

Electric Motors and Loudspeakers

Aha — one of the favourite exam topics of all time. Read it. Understand it. Learn it.

A Simple D.C. Electric Motor

4 Factors which Speed it up

1) More current
2) More turns on the coil
3) Stronger magnetic field
4) A soft iron core in the coil

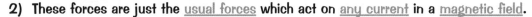

1) The diagram shows the <u>forces</u> acting on the two <u>side arms</u> of the <u>coil</u>.

2) These forces are just the <u>usual forces</u> which act on <u>any current</u> in a <u>magnetic field</u>.

3) Because the coil is on a <u>spindle</u> and the forces act <u>one up</u> and <u>one down</u>, it <u>rotates</u>.

4) The <u>split-ring commutator</u> is a clever way of <u>swapping</u> the contacts <u>every half turn</u> to keep the motor rotating in the <u>same direction</u>.

5) The direction of the motor can be <u>reversed</u> either by swapping the <u>polarity</u> of the <u>d.c. supply</u> or swapping the <u>magnetic poles</u> over.

6) The <u>speed</u> can be increased by adding <u>more turns</u> to the coil, increasing the <u>current</u>, increasing the <u>strength</u> of the magnetic <u>field</u> or by adding a <u>soft iron core</u>.

7) You can use Fleming's <u>left-hand rule</u> to work out which way the coil will <u>turn</u>.

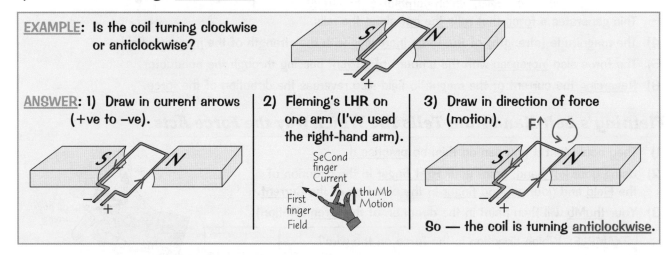

EXAMPLE: Is the coil turning clockwise or anticlockwise?

ANSWER: 1) Draw in current arrows (+ve to –ve).

2) Fleming's LHR on one arm (I've used the right-hand arm).
SeCond finger Current
First finger Field
thuMb Motion

3) Draw in direction of force (motion).
F
So — the coil is turning <u>anticlockwise</u>.

Loudspeakers Work Because of the Motor Effect

1) <u>A.c. electrical signals</u> from an <u>amplifier</u> are fed to a <u>coil of wire</u> in the <u>speaker</u>, which is wrapped around the base of a <u>cone</u>.

2) The coil is surrounded by a <u>permanent magnet</u>, so the a.c. signals cause a <u>force</u> on the coil and make it <u>move back and forth</u>.

3) These movements make the <u>cone vibrate</u> and this creates <u>sounds</u>.

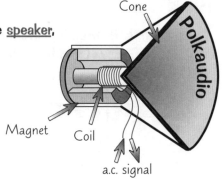

If a loudspeaker falls in the forest does it still make a sound...

Next time you're walking along listening to music think of the enjoyment that the motor effect is bringing you. Physics can make you happy. Keep going with the revision — good exam results can make you happy too.

Q1   State two ways to reverse the direction of rotation of a simple d.c. electric motor.   [2 marks]

Electromagnetic Induction

Generators use a pretty cool piece of physics to make electricity from the movement of a turbine. It's called electromagnetic (EM) induction — which basically means making electricity using a magnet.

> **ELECTROMAGNETIC INDUCTION:** The creation of a **VOLTAGE** (and maybe current) in a wire which is experiencing a **CHANGE IN MAGNETIC FIELD**.

The Dynamo Effect — Move the Wire or the Magnet

1) Using electromagnetic induction to generate electricity using energy from kinetic energy stores is called the dynamo effect. (In a power station, this energy is provided by the turbine.)

2) There are two different situations where you get EM induction:
   a) An electrical conductor (a coil of wire is often used) moves through a magnetic field.
   b) The magnetic field through an electrical conductor changes (gets bigger or smaller or reverses).

Electrical conductor moving in a magnetic field.

Induced voltage

Magnetic field through a conductor changing (as the magnet moves).

Ammeter

3) You can test this by connecting an ammeter to a conductor and moving the conductor through a magnetic field (or moving a magnet through the conductor). The ammeter will show the magnitude and direction of the induced current.

4) If the direction of movement is reversed, then the induced voltage/current will be reversed too.

> To get a bigger voltage, you can increase...
> 1) The **STRENGTH** of the **MAGNET**   3) The **SPEED** of movement
> 2) The number of **TURNS** on the **COIL**

Think about the simple electric motor — you've got a current in the wire and a magnetic field, which causes movement. Well, a generator works the opposite way round — you've got a magnetic field and movement, which induces a current.

A.C. Generators — Just Turn the Coil and There's a Current

You've already met generators and electromagnetic induction — this is a bit more detail about how a simple generator works.

1) Generators rotate a coil in a magnetic field (or a magnet in a coil).

2) Their construction is pretty much like a motor.

3) As the coil spins, a current is induced in the coil. This current changes direction every half turn.

4) Instead of a split-ring commutator, a.c. generators have slip rings and brushes so the contacts don't swap every half turn.

5) This means they produce a.c. voltage, as shown by these CRO displays. Note that faster revolutions produce not only more peaks but higher overall voltage too.

6) Power stations use a.c. generators to produce electricity — they just get the energy needed to turn the coil or magnetic field in different ways.

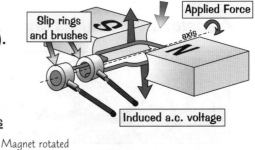

Coil rotated in a magnetic field.

Applied Force

Slip rings and brushes

axis

Induced a.c. voltage

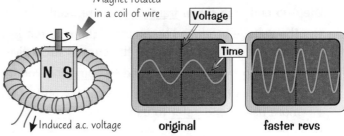

Magnet rotated in a coil of wire

Induced a.c. voltage

Voltage

Time

original   faster revs

How do you make a current in a pond — by in-duck-tion...

Induction's simple enough: conductor + magnetic field + movement = voltage (& current if there's a circuit).

Q1   What is electromagnetic induction?   [1 mark]

Transformers

Transformers only work with an alternating current. Try it with a standard battery and you'll be there for days.

Transformers Change the Voltage — but Only Alternating Voltages

1) Transformers change the size of the voltage of an alternating current.

2) They all have two coils, the primary and the secondary, joined with an iron core.

3) When an alternating voltage is applied across the primary coil, the magnetically soft (iron) core magnetises and demagnetises quickly. This induces an alternating voltage in the secondary coil (p.63).

4) The ratio between the primary and secondary voltages is the same as the ratio between the number of turns on the primary and secondary coils.

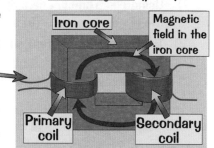

STEP-UP TRANSFORMERS increase the voltage. They have more turns on the secondary coil than the primary coil.

STEP-DOWN TRANSFORMERS decrease the voltage. They have more turns on the primary coil than the secondary.

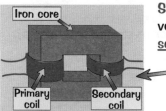

The Transformer Equation — Use it Either Way Up

1) You can calculate the output voltage from a transformer from the input voltage and the number of turns on each coil.

$$\frac{\text{Input (Primary) Voltage}}{\text{Output (Secondary) Voltage}} = \frac{\text{Number of turns on Primary}}{\text{Number of turns on Secondary}}$$

$$\frac{V_P}{V_S} = \frac{N_P}{N_S}$$

OR

$$\frac{V_S}{V_P} = \frac{N_S}{N_P}$$

2) This equation can be used either way up — there's less rearranging to do if you put whatever you're trying to calculate (the unknown) on the top.

3) The number of turns on the secondary coil divided by the number of turns on the primary coil is called the turns ratio.

Transformers are Nearly 100% Efficient So "Power In = Power Out"

The formula for power supplied is: Power = Voltage × Current or: $P = V \times I$.

So you can rewrite input power = output power as:

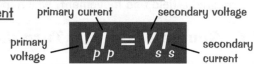

primary current   secondary voltage

$$V_P I_P = V_S I_S$$

primary voltage   secondary current

Transformers Make Transmitting Mains Electricity More Efficient

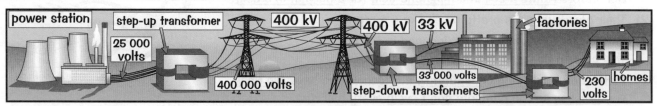

Step-up and step-down transformers are used when transmitting electricity across the country:

1) The voltage produced by power stations is too low to be transmitted efficiently. Power = VI, so the lower the voltage the higher the current for a given amount of power, and current causes wires to heat up.

2) A step-up transformer is used to boost the voltage before it is transmitted.

3) Step-down transformers are used at the end of the journey to reduce the voltage so it's more useful and safer to use.

I once had a dream about transforming into a hamster...

...but that's a story for another time. For now, better get revising what transformers do, and why they're useful.

Q1   A transformer with 320 turns on its primary coil and 770 turns on its secondary coil has a primary voltage of 65 V. Calculate the secondary voltage.   [3 marks]

Revision Questions for Section 6

Just what you were waiting for — a whole list of lovely questions to try. Better get them over with then...
- Try these questions and <u>tick off each one</u> when you <u>get it right</u>.
- When you've done <u>all the questions</u> for a topic and are <u>completely happy</u> with it, tick off the topic.

<u>Magnets and Magnetic Fields (p.59)</u> ☑

1) Sketch a diagram showing the magnetic field produced by a bar magnet.

2) Briefly describe an experiment to investigate the magnetic field pattern
    around a permanent bar magnet.

3) Sketch a diagram showing how you can produce a uniform magnetic field using two bar magnets.

<u>Electromagnetism (p.60-62)</u> ☑

4) Sketch the magnetic field produced by:
    a) A straight wire.   b) A flat loop of wire.   c) A solenoid.

5) What is an electromagnet?

6) Give one example of a soft magnetic material and one example of a hard magnetic material.

7) What's the motor effect?

8) What will happen to a charged particle moving through a magnetic field?

9) Name two factors that increase the strength of the force on a current-carrying wire in a magnetic field.

10) What's a split-ring commutator used for in an electric motor?

11) Sketch a labelled diagram of a loudspeaker and briefly explain how it works due to the motor effect.

<u>Electromagnetic Induction (p.63)</u> ☑

12) Briefly describe how a voltage can be induced using a coil of wire and a magnet.

13) Give three factors you could change to increase the size of an induced voltage.

14) Sketch a labelled diagram of an a.c. generator and briefly explain how it works.

<u>Transformers (p.64)</u> ☑

15) Sketch a diagram of a step-up transformer.

16) How does a transformer change the voltage of an electricity supply?

17) A transformer has 10 turns on the primary coil and 50 turns on the secondary coil.
    If the primary voltage is 30 V, what will the secondary voltage be?

18) The power output of a transformer is 6000 W.
    If the input voltage is 30 000 V, what is the input current?

19) How are transformers used in the transmission of electricity across long distances?

Radioactivity

Although you can't <u>see</u> it, <u>nuclear radiation</u> is <u>all around us</u> all the time — important stuff if you ask me.

At the Centre of Every Atom is a Nucleus

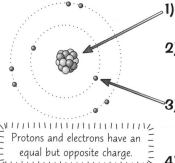

Protons and electrons have an equal but opposite charge.

1) The <u>nucleus</u> of an atom contains <u>protons</u> and <u>neutrons</u>. It makes up most of the <u>mass</u> of the atom, but takes up <u>virtually no space</u> — it's <u>tiny</u>.

2) The number of <u>protons</u> in the nucleus is called the <u>atomic number</u>, or <u>proton number</u>. The <u>total</u> number of <u>protons and neutrons</u> in the nucleus is called the <u>mass number</u>, or <u>nucleon number</u>.

3) The <u>electrons</u> are <u>negatively charged</u> and really really <u>small</u>. They whizz around the <u>outside</u> of the atom. Their <u>paths take up a lot of space</u>, giving the atom its <u>overall size</u> (though it's <u>mostly empty space</u>).

A Tom.

4) Atoms are <u>neutral</u>, so the <u>number of protons = the number of electrons</u>.

Isotopes are Atoms with Different Numbers of Neutrons

1) Many elements have a few different <u>isotopes</u>. Isotopes are atoms with the <u>same</u> number of <u>protons</u> (i.e. the <u>same</u> atomic number) but a <u>different</u> number of <u>neutrons</u> (so a <u>different</u> mass number).

2) E.g. there are two common isotopes of carbon. Carbon-14 has two more neutrons than 'normal' carbon (carbon-12).

3) Usually each element only has one or two <u>stable isotopes</u> — like carbon-12. The other isotopes tend to be <u>radioactive</u> — the nucleus is <u>unstable</u>, so it <u>decays</u> (breaks down) and emits <u>radiation</u>. Carbon-14 is an <u>unstable isotope</u> of carbon.

$^{12}_{6}C$ mass number / atomic number $^{14}_{6}C$

6 protons and 6 neutrons so it's carbon-12

6 protons and 8 neutrons so it's carbon-14

Radioactive Decay is a Random Process

1) The nuclei of <u>unstable</u> isotopes break down at <u>random</u>. If you have 1000 unstable nuclei, you can't say when any <u>one of them</u> is going to decay, and you can't do anything at all to <u>make a decay happen</u>.

2) Each nucleus just decays quite <u>spontaneously</u> in its <u>own good time</u>. It's completely unaffected by <u>physical</u> conditions like <u>temperature</u> or by any sort of <u>chemical bonding</u> etc.

3) When the nucleus <u>does</u> decay it <u>spits out</u> one or more types of radiation — <u>alpha</u> (α), <u>beta</u> (β^-), <u>gamma</u> (γ) or <u>neutrons</u> (n) (see next page).

4) In the process, the <u>nucleus</u> often <u>changes</u> into a <u>new element</u>.

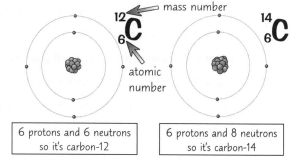

Uranium-238   Thorium-234   Alpha decay α particle
γ ray emitted

Carbon-14   Beta decay   Nitrogen-14 β^- particle

Background Radiation is Everywhere All the Time

There's (low-level) <u>background nuclear radiation</u> all around us all the time. It comes from:

- substances here on <u>Earth</u> — some radioactivity comes from air, food, building materials, soil, rocks...
- radiation from <u>space</u> (cosmic rays) — mostly from the Sun,
- <u>living things</u> — there's a little bit of radioactive material in all living things,
- radiation due to <u>human activity</u> — e.g. fallout from nuclear explosions, or nuclear waste (though this is usually a tiny proportion of the total background radiation).

Isotopes of an outfit — same dress, different accessories...

Lots of new words to remember on this page. Isotopes, atomic number, alpha, beta.... make sure you know them all.

Q1   Which of the following represents an isotope of $^{14}_{7}N$: $^{15}_{7}N$ or $^{14}_{8}N$? Explain your answer.   [2 marks]

Ionising Radiation

Alpha, beta and gamma are three types of ionising radiation. You need to remember <u>what</u> they are, how well they <u>penetrate</u> materials (including air), and their <u>ionising</u> power.

Nuclear Radiation Causes Ionisation

1) Nuclear radiation causes <u>ionisation</u> by <u>bashing into atoms</u> and <u>knocking electrons off</u> them. Atoms (with <u>no overall charge</u>) are turned into <u>ions</u> (which are <u>charged</u>) — hence the term "<u>ionisation</u>".

2) There's a pattern: the <u>further</u> the radiation can <u>penetrate</u> before hitting an atom and getting stopped, the <u>less damage</u> it will do along the way and so the <u>less ionising</u> it is.

3) Ionising radiation can be detected using either a <u>Geiger-Müller detector</u> (see p.68) or <u>photographic film</u>.

4) You need to know lots of details about <u>three different types</u> of ionising radiation:

Alpha Particles are Helium Nuclei $\quad ^4_2\text{He}$

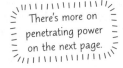
There's more on penetrating power on the next page.

1) Alpha (α) particles are made up of <u>2 protons and 2 neutrons</u> — they're <u>big</u>, <u>heavy</u> and <u>slow-moving</u>.

2) They therefore <u>don't penetrate</u> far into materials but are <u>stopped quickly</u>.

3) Because of their size they're <u>strongly ionising</u>, which means they <u>bash into a lot of atoms</u> and <u>knock electrons off</u> them before they slow down, which creates lots of ions.

4) Because they're electrically <u>charged</u> (with a positive charge), alpha particles are <u>deflected</u> (their <u>direction changes</u>) by <u>electric</u> and <u>magnetic fields</u>.

5) Emitting an alpha particle <u>decreases</u> the <u>atomic</u> number of the nucleus by <u>2</u> and the <u>mass</u> number by <u>4</u>.

See page 68 for more.

Beta Particles are Electrons $\quad ^{\;\;0}_{-1}\text{e}^-$

1) A beta (β^-) particle is an <u>electron</u> which has been emitted from the <u>nucleus</u> of an atom when a <u>neutron</u> turns into a <u>proton</u> and an <u>electron</u>.

2) When a <u>beta particle</u> is emitted, the number of <u>protons</u> in the nucleus increases by 1. So the <u>atomic</u> number <u>increases</u> by <u>1</u> but the <u>mass</u> number <u>stays the same</u> (p.68).

3) They move <u>quite fast</u> and they are <u>quite small</u>.

4) They <u>penetrate moderately</u> before colliding and are <u>moderately ionising</u> too.

5) Because they're <u>charged</u> (negatively), beta particles are <u>deflected</u> by electric and magnetic fields.

Neutron radiation (where neutrons are emitted) is ionising too, but you don't need to know its properties — only how to balance neutron decay equations (see p.68).

Gamma Rays are Very Short Wavelength EM Waves

1) In a way, gamma (γ) rays are the <u>opposite of alpha particles</u>. They have <u>no mass</u> — they're just <u>energy</u> (in the form of an EM wave — see p.28).

2) They can <u>penetrate a long way</u> into materials without being stopped.

3) This means they are <u>weakly ionising</u> because they tend to <u>pass through</u> rather than collide with atoms. But eventually they <u>hit something</u> and do <u>damage</u>.

4) Gamma rays have <u>no charge</u>, so they're <u>not deflected</u> by electric or magnetic fields.

5) Gamma emission always happens after beta or alpha decay. You <u>never</u> get <u>just gamma</u> rays emitted.

6) Gamma ray emission has <u>no effect</u> on the atomic or mass numbers of the isotope (p.68). If a nucleus has <u>excess energy</u>, it loses this energy by emitting a gamma ray.

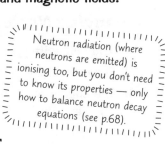

Learn your alphabet-agamma...

Make sure you remember what each particle is made up of. It'll help you balance nuclear equations on the next page.

Q1   Explain what is meant by ionisation. [1 mark]

Q2   Name four types of ionising radiation. [1 mark]

Investigating Radiation & Nuclear Equations

As you've seen, <u>different radiation</u> can penetrate by different amounts.
This means that they can <u>pass through</u> different materials. Don't believe me? Ok, you try it.

You Can Identify the Type by its Penetrating Power

1) <u>Alpha particles</u> are blocked by <u>paper</u>, <u>skin</u>, or a few cm of <u>air</u>.

2) <u>Beta particles</u> are blocked by <u>thin metal</u>.

3) <u>Gamma rays</u> are blocked by <u>thick lead</u> or <u>very thick concrete</u>.

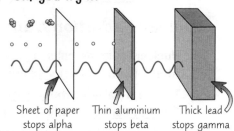

Sheet of paper stops alpha | Thin aluminium stops beta | Thick lead stops gamma

You can Investigate the Penetration of Radiation

PRACTICAL

1) You can <u>detect</u> ionising radiation with a <u>Geiger-Müller detector</u>. A Geiger-Müller detector gives a <u>count rate</u> — the number of <u>radioactive particles</u> reaching it per second.

Geiger-Müller detector

radioactive source

radiation

material

2) Set up the equipment as shown on the right, so that when nothing is placed between the source and detector, the counter records a <u>high count rate</u>.

3) Remove the source to measure the <u>background count</u> (p.66) over a time period (e.g. 30 seconds). <u>Divide</u> your count by the time period to get a <u>background count</u> rate (in counts per second). Do this three times and find the mean. <u>Subtract</u> this from all your results.

4) <u>Replace</u> the source and measure the count rate (<u>minus</u> the background count rate) with <u>no material present</u> three times and take a mean. Then insert <u>different materials</u> between the source and detector. Record the count rate for each material three times and find the mean.

5) If the count rate remains about <u>the same</u> when the material is inserted, then the radiation can <u>penetrate</u> the material. If it <u>drops</u> by a large amount, then the radiation is being <u>absorbed</u> and blocked by the material. If it drops to <u>zero</u> after the background count is subtracted, the radiation is being <u>completely absorbed</u>.

6) Repeat this experiment with <u>different sources</u> to investigate the penetrations of different kinds of radiation.

Radioactive sources can be dangerous if you don't use them properly (p.71):
* Radioactive sources should be kept in a <u>lead-lined box</u> when not in use.
* They should only be picked up using <u>long-handled tongs</u> or <u>forceps</u>.
* Take care not to <u>point</u> them at anyone, and keep a <u>safe distance</u> from them.

\\\\\\|||||||||||||||||||||||||///
You can also investigate this using a computerised radiation simulator. Doing it in the lab requires lots of work with dangerous radioactive sources, so you might have simulated it in class instead.
//////||||||||||||||||||\\\\\\

Balancing Nuclear Equations

1) You can write <u>equations</u> for <u>nuclear reactions</u> — just like you can for chemical reactions.

2) The overall <u>charge</u> and <u>mass</u> have to <u>be the same</u> after a nuclear reaction as they were <u>before</u>.

3) The charge on a nucleus or particle is <u>equal to</u> the atomic number, and its mass is <u>equal to</u> the mass number. So the totals of the <u>atomic</u> and <u>mass</u> numbers <u>have</u> to be the <u>same</u> on <u>both sides</u> of the equation:

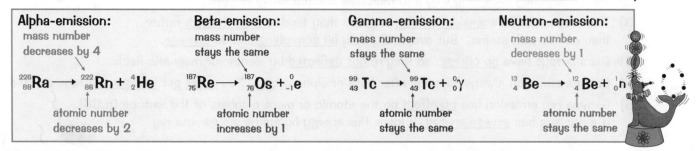

Alpha-emission:	Beta-emission:	Gamma-emission:	Neutron-emission:
mass number decreases by 4	mass number stays the same	mass number stays the same	mass number decreases by 1
$^{226}_{88}\text{Ra} \longrightarrow \, ^{222}_{86}\text{Rn} + \, ^{4}_{2}\text{He}$	$^{187}_{75}\text{Re} \longrightarrow \, ^{187}_{76}\text{Os} + \, ^{0}_{-1}\text{e}$	$^{99}_{43}\text{Tc} \longrightarrow \, ^{99}_{43}\text{Tc} + \, ^{0}_{0}\gamma$	$^{13}_{4}\text{Be} \longrightarrow \, ^{12}_{4}\text{Be} + \, ^{1}_{0}\text{n}$
atomic number decreases by 2	atomic number increases by 1	atomic number stays the same	atomic number stays the same

Keep balanced during revision and practise nuclear equations...

Nuclear equations are simple, but that doesn't mean you shouldn't practise them. Try these questions on for size.

Q1   What type of radiation is given off in this decay? $^{8}_{3}\text{Li} \rightarrow \, ^{8}_{4}\text{Be} + \text{radiation}$.   [1 mark]

Q2   Write the nuclear equation for $^{219}_{86}\text{Rn}$ decaying to polonium (Po) by emitting an alpha particle.   [3 marks]

Half-Life

Half-life is the <u>time</u> it takes for a radioactive material to lose <u>half</u> of its radioactivity. Simple really.

The Radioactivity of a Sample Always Decreases Over Time

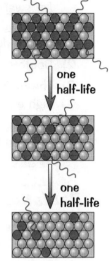

1) This is <u>pretty obvious</u> when you think about it. Each time a <u>decay</u> happens and an alpha or beta particle or gamma ray is given out, it means one more <u>radioactive nucleus</u> has <u>disappeared</u>.

2) Obviously, as the <u>unstable nuclei</u> all disappear, the <u>activity</u> (the number of decays in a given time) will <u>decrease</u>. So the <u>older</u> a sample becomes, the <u>less radiation</u> it will emit.

3) <u>How quickly</u> the activity <u>drops off</u> varies a lot. For <u>some isotopes</u> it takes <u>just a few hours</u> before nearly all the unstable nuclei have <u>decayed</u>, whilst others last for <u>millions of years</u>.

one half-life

4) The problem with trying to <u>measure</u> this is that <u>the activity never reaches zero</u>, which is why we have to use the idea of <u>half-life</u> to measure how quickly the activity <u>drops off</u>.

5) Learn this <u>important definition</u> of half-life:

> <u>Half-life</u> is the <u>time taken</u> for <u>half</u> of the <u>radioactive atoms</u> now present to <u>decay</u>.

one half-life

6) Another definition of half-life is: "<u>The time taken for the activity (or count rate) to fall by half</u>". Use either.

7) A <u>short half-life</u> means the <u>activity falls quickly</u>, because <u>lots</u> of the nuclei decay <u>quickly</u>.

8) A <u>long half-life</u> means the activity <u>falls more slowly</u> because <u>most</u> of the nuclei don't decay for <u>a long time</u> — they just sit there, <u>basically unstable</u>, but kind of <u>biding their time</u>.

For any particular isotope, the half-life is always the same.

Example: The activity of a radioactive isotope is 640 Bq. Two hours later it has fallen to 40 Bq. Find the half-life of the sample.

Radioactivity is measured in becquerels (Bq). 1 Bq is 1 decay per second.

To answer, go through it in <u>short simple steps</u> like this:

INITIAL count:		after ONE half-life:		after TWO half-lives:		after THREE half-lives:		after FOUR half-lives:
640	$(\div 2) \rightarrow$	320	$(\div 2) \rightarrow$	160	$(\div 2) \rightarrow$	80	$(\div 2) \rightarrow$	40

Notice the careful <u>step-by-step method</u>, which tells us it takes <u>four half-lives</u> for the activity to fall from 640 to 40. So <u>two hours</u> represents four half-lives, so the <u>half-life is 30 minutes</u>.

Measuring the Half-Life of a Sample Using a Graph

Activity (Bq)

1) This can <u>only be done</u> by taking <u>several readings</u> of a source's activity, usually using a <u>Geiger-Müller (G-M) detector</u>. The results can then be <u>plotted</u> as a <u>graph</u>, which will <u>always</u> be shaped like this.

Each of these sections is one half-life. So the half-life is 2 seconds.

2) The <u>half-life</u> is found from the graph, by finding the <u>time interval</u> on the <u>bottom axis</u> corresponding to a <u>halving</u> of the <u>activity</u> on the <u>vertical axis</u>. Easy peasy really.

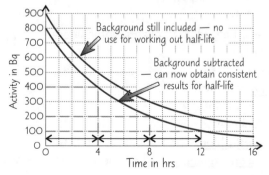

Background still included — no use for working out half-life

Background subtracted — can now obtain consistent results for half-life

You need to make sure you've <u>subtracted</u> the <u>background count</u> from your readings before you plot the graph (see p.66). If you don't, you'll get an <u>incorrect value</u> for half-life, and it'll be <u>different</u> for each measurement you take from the graph. Realistically, the only difficult bit is actually <u>remembering</u> about that for your exam, should they ask you about it. They could also test that idea in a <u>calculation</u> question.

Half-life of a box of chocolates — about five minutes...

Half-life — the time for the number of radioactive nuclei, the activity or the count-rate to halve. Simple.

Q1   The initial activity of a sample is 40 Bq. Calculate the count-rate after three half-lives.   [2 marks]

Uses of Nuclear Radiation

Nuclear radiation can be <u>really</u> useful — but you've got to be careful about what <u>isotope</u> you choose to use.

Medical Tracers Use Beta or Gamma Radiation

Beta and gamma will <u>penetrate</u> the skin and other body tissues. This makes them suitable as <u>medical tracers</u>:

1) A source which emits beta or gamma radiation is <u>injected</u> into the patient (or <u>swallowed</u>). The radiation penetrates the body tissues and can be <u>detected externally</u>. As the source moves around the body, the radiographer uses a detector and a computer to monitor its progress on a display.

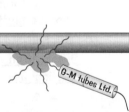

Iodine-123 collecting in the thyroid gland.

Gamma rays

Radiation detector

2) Doctors use this method to check whether the <u>organs</u> of the body are working as they should.

3) The radioactive source has to have a <u>short half-life</u>, so that the initial levels are high enough to be easily <u>detected</u>, but the radioactivity inside the patient <u>quickly disappears</u>.

4) An <u>alpha</u> source would be <u>worse than useless</u> as a medical tracer — <u>useless</u> because it would be stopped by the body's tissues, so you'd never detect it externally, and <u>worse</u> than useless because its <u>strong ionising</u> power makes alpha radiation really <u>harmful</u> if it gets <u>inside</u> you (see page 71).

Radiation is Also Used to Treat Cancer

1) You'll see on the next page that <u>ionising radiation</u> can kill or damage cells and tissues, which can cause <u>cancer</u>. But once the cancer's started, ionising radiation can <u>also</u> be used to <u>treat</u> it.

2) <u>Radiotherapy</u> kills the cancer cells and stops them dividing — it involves using a <u>high</u> dose of gamma rays, carefully directed to zap the cells in the <u>tumour</u> while minimising the dose to the rest of the body.

Food and Equipment can be Sterilised Using Gamma Rays

1) <u>Food</u> can be <u>irradiated</u> with (p.71) a <u>high dose</u> of <u>gamma rays</u> to <u>kill</u> all <u>microbes</u>, so that it doesn't go bad as quickly as it would do otherwise.

unsterilised → gamma source → sterilised

2) Similarly, <u>medical equipment</u> can be <u>sterilised</u> using gamma rays.

3) <u>Irradiation</u> is a particularly good method of sterilisation because, unlike boiling, it doesn't involve <u>high temperatures</u>, so <u>fresh fruit</u> or <u>plastic instruments</u> can be totally <u>sterilised</u> without being <u>damaged</u>.

4) The radioactive source used for this needs to be a <u>very strong</u> emitter of <u>gamma rays</u> with a <u>reasonably long half-life</u> (at least several months) so that it doesn't need <u>replacing</u> too often.

Radiation is Used in Industry for Tracers and Thickness Gauges

1) <u>Gamma emitting tracers</u> are used in <u>industry</u> to detect <u>leaks</u> in <u>underground pipes</u>.

2) The source is allowed to flow down the pipe and a <u>detector</u> is used above ground. Gamma is used because it can pass through any <u>rocks or earth</u> surrounding the pipe.

3) If there's a <u>crack</u> in the pipe, more radiation will collect outside the pipe, and the detector will show <u>extra high</u> radioactivity at that point.

G-M tubes Ltd.

4) It should have a <u>short half-life</u> so as not to cause a long-term <u>hazard</u> if it collects somewhere.

5) <u>Beta radiation</u> is used in <u>thickness control</u>. You direct radiation through the stuff being made (e.g. paper), and put a detector on the other side, connected to a control unit. When the <u>detected</u> radiation level changes, it means the paper is coming out too thick or too thin, so the control unit adjusts the rollers to give the correct thickness.

rollers

paper

beta source

control unit

processor unit

detector

6) It needs to be a <u>beta</u> source, because then the paper will <u>partly block</u> the radiation (see p.68). If it <u>all</u> goes through (or <u>none</u> of it does), then the reading <u>won't change</u> at all as the thickness changes.

Choose your source carefully — I like ketchup on ice cream...

To make use of radiation, you've got to match the requirements of the job to the properties of your source.

Q1   Explain why sources of alpha radiation cannot used to measure the thickness of aluminium.   [2 marks]

Risks from Nuclear Radiation

Radiation's dangerous and useful at the same time — it can both cause and cure cancer, for instance.

Ionising Radiation Can Damage Cells and Tissues

1) Beta and gamma can penetrate the skin and soft tissues to reach the delicate organs inside the body. This makes beta and gamma sources more hazardous than alpha when outside the body. If they get inside (e.g. swallowed or breathed in), their radiation mostly passes straight out without doing much damage.

2) Alpha radiation can't penetrate the skin, but it's very dangerous if it gets inside the body. Alpha sources do all their damage in a very localised area.

3) When radiation enters your body, it will collide with molecules in your cells. These collisions cause ionisation, which damages or destroys the molecules. The extent of the harmful effects depends on how much exposure you have to the radiation, and its energy and penetration.

4) Lower doses tend to cause minor damage without killing the cell. This can cause mutations in cells which then divide uncontrollably — this is cancer.

5) Higher doses tend to kill cells completely, causing radiation sickness if a large part of your body is affected at the same time.

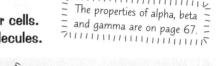
The properties of alpha, beta and gamma are on page 67.

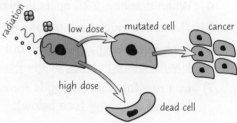

Exposure to Radiation is called Irradiation

1) Objects near a radioactive source are irradiated by it. This simply means they're exposed to it (we're always being irradiated by background radiation sources).

2) Irradiating something does not make it radioactive (and won't turn you into a superhero).

3) Keeping sources in lead-lined boxes, standing behind barriers or being in a different room and using remote-controlled arms are all ways of reducing the risk of irradiation.

Contamination is Radioactive Particles Getting onto Objects

1) If unwanted radioactive atoms get onto or into an object, the object is said to be contaminated. E.g. if you touch a radioactive source without wearing gloves, your hands would be contaminated.

2) These contaminating atoms might then decay, releasing radiation which could cause you harm.

3) Contamination is especially dangerous because radioactive particles could get inside your body.

4) Gloves and tongs should be used when handling sources, to avoid particles getting stuck to your skin or under your nails. Some industrial workers wear protective suits and masks to stop them breathing in particles.

Radioactive Waste is Difficult to Dispose of Safely

1) Most radioactive waste from nuclear power stations and hospitals is 'low-level' (slightly radioactive) — things like clothing, syringes, etc. This kind of waste can be disposed of by burying it in secure landfill sites.

2) High-level waste is the really dangerous stuff — a lot of it stays highly radioactive for tens of thousands of years, and so has to be treated very carefully. It's often sealed into glass blocks, which are then sealed in metal canisters. These could then be buried deep underground.

3) However, it's difficult to find suitable places to bury high-level waste. The site has to be geologically stable (e.g. not suffer from earthquakes), since big movements in the rock could disturb the canisters and allow radioactive material to leak out. If this material gets into the groundwater, it could contaminate the soil, plants, rivers, etc., and get into our drinking water.

Failing your exams would be a high-level waste of time...

Make sure you can describe how to reduce the risks of nuclear radiation, and why it's so important that you do.

Q1 Explain the difference between contamination and irradiation. [1 mark]

Q2 Give three safety measures that should be followed to avoid the risk of irradiation [2 marks]

Nuclear Fission and Fusion

Loads of energy's released either when you break apart <u>really big nuclei</u> or join together <u>really small nuclei</u>.

Nuclear Power Stations use Nuclear Fission Chain Reactions

1) <u>Nuclear fission</u> is the <u>splitting</u> of an atom, which releases <u>energy</u>. It can be <u>spontaneous</u>, but in a nuclear reactor it's made to happen — e.g. to <u>uranium-235</u>.

2) If a <u>slow-moving neutron</u> is absorbed by a uranium-235 nucleus, the nucleus can <u>split</u>.

3) Each time this happens, it spits out a <u>small number of neutrons</u>. These might go on to hit other uranium-235 nuclei, causing them to split also... and so on and so on. This is a <u>chain reaction</u>.

4) When uranium-235 splits in two it will form <u>two</u> new <u>daughter nuclei</u>, both <u>lighter elements</u> than uranium.

5) These new nuclei are usually <u>radioactive</u>. This is the <u>big problem</u> with nuclear power — <u>radioactive waste</u>.

6) Each nucleus <u>splitting</u> gives out <u>a lot of energy</u> — this energy is in the <u>kinetic energy stores</u> of the <u>fission products</u> (the daughter nuclei and the neutrons).

7) In a reactor, this energy is transferred to <u>thermal energy stores</u> to produce <u>steam</u> to drive a <u>turbine</u> (see below).

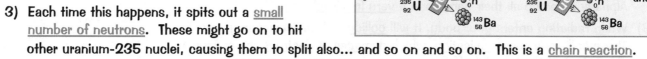

Nuclear Reactors Have to Work Safely

1) The <u>neutrons</u> released by fission reactions in a nuclear reactor have <u>a lot</u> of energy. In order to be <u>absorbed</u> by uranium nuclei and <u>sustain</u> the chain reaction, they need to be <u>slowed down</u>.

2) The <u>moderator</u>, usually graphite or water, <u>slows</u> down <u>neutrons</u>.

3) <u>Control rods</u>, often made of <u>boron</u>, limit the rate of fission by <u>absorbing</u> excess neutrons.

4) The <u>high-energy</u> neutrons and <u>gamma rays</u> (energy) released in fission are highly penetrating <u>ionising radiation</u>. <u>Shielding</u> has to be used to <u>absorb</u> the ionising radiation. The shielding is usually a <u>thick concrete</u> structure, which may also contain <u>lead</u> or other metals.

5) A substance (e.g. CO_2) pumped round the reactor <u>transfers</u> the energy (by heating) to the water in the <u>heat exchanger</u>. The water turns to <u>steam</u>, which turns a <u>turbine</u>, which turns a <u>generator</u> and generates <u>electricity</u>.

Nuclear Fusion — Joining Small Nuclei

1) <u>Nuclear fusion</u> is the opposite of nuclear fission. In nuclear fusion, two <u>light nuclei collide</u> at high speed and <u>join</u> (fuse) to create a <u>larger</u>, heavier nucleus. E.g. <u>hydrogen</u> nuclei can fuse to produce a <u>helium nucleus</u>.

2) This <u>heavier</u> nucleus doesn't have as much <u>mass</u> as the two <u>separate</u>, light nuclei did. Some of the mass of the lighter nuclei is converted to <u>energy</u> (<u>don't panic</u>, you don't need to know <u>how</u>). This energy is then <u>released</u> as radiation.

3) Fusion releases <u>a lot</u> of energy (more than fission for a given mass of fuel) — all the energy released in <u>stars</u> comes from fusion.

4) The <u>big problem</u> is that fusion only happens at <u>really high pressures and temperatures</u> (about <u>10 000 000 °C</u>). This is because the <u>positively charged</u> nuclei have to get <u>very close</u> to fuse, so they need to be moving <u>very fast</u> to overcome the strong <u>force</u> due to <u>electrostatic repulsion</u> (p.23).

5) So far, scientists haven't found a way of using fusion to generate energy for us to use. The <u>temperatures</u> and <u>pressures</u> needed for fusion are so <u>high</u> that fusion reactors are really <u>hard</u> and <u>expensive</u> to build.

BEWARE: the filling of this fruit pie is hotter than the conditions needed for fusion.

Pity they can't release energy by confusion...*

Nuclear reactors are carefully-designed to release energy safely, but we've not worked out how to do that with fusion yet.

Q1 Draw a diagram showing how fission can lead to a chain reaction. [3 marks]

Q2 Explain why fusion only occurs at high temperatures and pressures. [2 marks]

*There'd be plenty of physics books to use as fuel.

Revision Questions for Section 7

Well, that wraps up Section 7. Now a reward for ploughing through loads of pages of pretty intense science — a page of lovely questions. Okay, I know it seems a little daunting, but it's absolutely vital to check that you've learnt all the right stuff..

- Try these questions and tick off each one when you get it right.
- When you've done all the questions for a topic and are completely happy with it, tick off the topic.

Nuclear Radiation (p.66-68) ☑

1) What is the atomic number of a nucleus?
2) What is the mass number of a nucleus?
3) What are isotopes of an element?
4) Name four things that may be emitted during radioactive decay.
5) Briefly describe what background radiation is and where it comes from.
6) Describe what alpha, beta and gamma radiation are.
7) Which is the most ionising out of alpha, beta and gamma radiation?
8) Describe how the mass and atomic numbers of an atom change if it emits an alpha particle.
9) In what type of nuclear decay does a neutron change into a proton within the nucleus?
10) What type of nuclear decay doesn't change the mass or charge of the nucleus?
11) What type of radiation is stopped by paper?
12) Give two ways you can detect ionising radiation.
13) What quantities need to be the same on each side of a nuclear equation?

Half-life (p.69) ☑

14) What is meant by the 'activity' of a radioactive source?
15) Define half-life.
16) True or false? A short half-life means a small proportion of the atoms are decaying per second.

Uses and Risks of Nuclear Radiation (p.70-71) ☑

17) Briefly describe two uses of nuclear radiation in medicine.
18) Explain why alpha radiation could not be used to check the thickness of metal sheets.
19) Other than thickness gauges, give one other use of nuclear radiation in industry.
20) Why is nuclear radiation dangerous to living organisms?
21) Explain why radioactive waste is difficult to dispose of safely.

Fusion and Fission (p.72) ☑

22) What are the products of the nuclear fission of uranium-235?
23) True or false? The fission products of uranium-235 are also radioactive.
24) Briefly describe how a chain reaction is set up in a nuclear reactor.
25) What job do control rods, moderators and shielding do in a nuclear reactor?
26) State the conditions needed to create a fusion reaction.

The Universe

There's all sorts of exciting stuff in the universe... Our whole solar system is just part of a huge galaxy. And there are billions upon billions of galaxies. You should be realising now that the universe is pretty darn big...

We are Part of the Milky Way Galaxy

1) The universe is a large collection of billions of galaxies.

2) A galaxy is a large collection of stars.

3) Our Sun is just one of many billions of stars which form the Milky Way galaxy. Our Sun is about halfway along one of the spiral arms of the Milky Way.

4) The distance between neighbouring stars in the galaxy is often millions of times greater than the distance between planets in our solar system.

5) The force which keeps the stars together in a galaxy is gravity, of course. And like most things in the universe, galaxies rotate — a bit like a Catherine wheel.

6) Galaxies themselves are often millions of times further apart than the stars are within a galaxy.

7) So the universe is mostly empty space and is really, really BIG.

You are here.

Our Solar System has One Star — The Sun

A satellite is an object that orbits a second, more massive object.

Our solar system is all the stuff that orbits the Sun. This includes things like:

1) Planets — these are large objects that orbit a star. The eight planets in our solar system are, in order (from the Sun outwards): Mercury, Venus, Earth, Mars, Jupiter, Saturn, Uranus and Neptune.

2) Dwarf planets, like our pal Pluto. These are planet-like objects that aren't big enough to be planets.

3) Moons — these orbit planets with almost circular orbits. They're a type of natural satellite (i.e. they're not man-made).

4) Artificial satellites (ones humans have built) that usually orbit the Earth in fairly circular orbits.

5) Asteroids — lumps of rock and metal that orbit the Sun. They're usually found in the asteroid belt.

6) Comets — lumps of ice and dust that orbit the Sun. Their orbits are usually highly elliptical (a very stretched out circle) — some travel from near to the Sun to the outskirts of our solar system.

Gravity Provides the Force That Creates Orbits

1) The planets move around the Sun in almost circular orbits (same goes for the Moon around the Earth).

2) If an object is travelling in a circle it is constantly changing direction (and so constantly accelerating), which means there must be a force acting on it.

3) The force causing this is a centripetal force. It acts towards the centre of the circle.

4) This force would cause the object to just fall towards whatever it was orbiting, but as the object is already moving, it just causes it to change its direction.

5) The object keeps accelerating towards what it's orbiting but the instantaneous velocity (which is at a right angle to the acceleration) keeps it travelling in a circle.

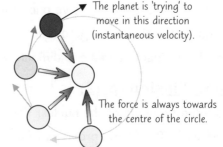

The planet is 'trying' to move in this direction (instantaneous velocity).

The force is always towards the centre of the circle.

6) The force that makes this happen is provided by the gravitational force (gravity). The gravitational attraction of the Sun keeps the planets and comets in their orbits around it.

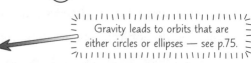

Gravity leads to orbits that are either circles or ellipses — see p.75.

7) Satellites are kept in their orbits around planets by the gravitational attraction of the planet.

Revision's hard work — you've got to plan et...

Make sure you know what orbits what and how to tell a moon from a planet. Then have a go at these questions.

Q1   Give the name of the galaxy that our solar system is located in.   [1 mark]

Q2   Explain how the gravitational force keeps an object in orbit.   [3 marks]

Gravity and Orbits

So as well as keeping you grounded, <u>gravity</u> also keeps the <u>Earth</u> moving around the <u>Sun</u>. Nifty stuff.

The Force due to Gravity Depends on Mass and Distance

1) Back on page 3 you saw that the <u>weight</u> (i.e. the <u>force</u> on an object due to gravity) of any object varies depending on the <u>strength</u> (*g*) of the <u>gravitational field</u> that it is in.

2) <u>Gravitational field strength</u> depends on the <u>mass</u> of the body <u>creating</u> the field. The <u>larger</u> the mass of the body, the <u>stronger</u> its gravitational field. (The Earth is <u>more massive</u> than the Moon, so an object would <u>weigh more</u> on Earth than it would on the Moon.)

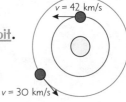

The fact that different planets orbit the Sun at different speeds means that the distances between planets vary over time.

3) Gravitational field strength also varies with <u>distance</u>. The <u>closer</u> you get to a star or planet, the <u>stronger</u> the <u>gravitational force</u> is.

4) The <u>stronger</u> the force, the <u>larger</u> the <u>instantaneous velocity</u> needed to <u>balance</u> it.

5) So the <u>closer</u> to a star or planet you get, the <u>faster</u> you need to go to remain in <u>orbit</u>.

6) For an object in a <u>stable orbit</u>, if the <u>speed</u> of the object <u>changes</u>, the <u>size</u> (<u>radius</u>) of its <u>orbit</u> must do so too. <u>Faster</u> moving objects will move in a <u>stable</u> orbit with a <u>smaller radius</u> than <u>slower</u> moving ones.

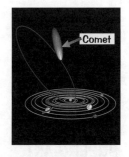

v = 42 km/s

v = 30 km/s

There are Different Types of Orbit

1) The orbits of moons and planets are usually <u>slightly elliptical</u>.

2) Comets orbit the Sun, but have very <u>elliptical</u> (elongated) orbits with the Sun <u>at one focus</u> (near one end of the orbit).

3) Comets have orbital periods much <u>longer</u> than the Earth, as they travel from the <u>outer edges</u> of our solar system. A comet travels <u>much faster</u> when it's <u>nearer the Sun</u> than it does in the more <u>distant</u> parts of its orbit. That's because the <u>increased pull</u> of gravity makes it <u>speed up</u> the closer it gets to the Sun.

4) Some artificial Earth satellites have an orbital period of exactly <u>one day</u>. They're called <u>geostationary</u> satellites, and are useful in <u>communications</u> because they're always over the same part of the planet.

Comet

You can Calculate Orbital Speeds

1) You can calculate the <u>speed of an orbit</u> using the formula from page 1:

$$speed = \frac{distance}{time}$$

2) For a <u>circular orbit</u>, the <u>distance</u> travelled is the <u>circumference</u> of the orbit, which is given by the formula:

distance = 2 × π × radius of orbit

3) So the formula for the <u>speed of an orbit</u> is:

$$orbital\ speed = \frac{2 \times \pi \times orbital\ radius}{time\ period} \qquad v = \frac{2\pi r}{T}$$

Remember that '*r*' is the distance between the centre of the planet or star and the object that is orbiting around it.

Example: Calculate the speed of a satellite orbiting above the Earth's surface at an altitude of 600 km. The radius of the Earth is 6400 km and the satellite takes 200 mins to orbit the Earth once.

First calculate *r* in m, *r* = 6400 + 600 = 7000 km = 7 000 000 m

Then find the time period in seconds, *T* = 200 × 60 = 12 000 s

So orbital speed, $v = \dfrac{2 \times \pi \times 7\,000\,000}{12\,000} = 3665.191...$ m/s = 3700 m/s (to 2 s.f.)

Forget the Sun, I'm pretty sure everything revolves around me...

Make sure you get your head around all this stuff about orbits — it's all about balancing the gravitational force and the object's speed. You'll be given the equation above in the exam, so you don't need to learn it, just know how to use it.

Q1   Calculate the orbital radius of a moon which orbits a planet in 30 hours with a speed of 1400 m/s.   [3 marks]

Stellar Evolution

Stars go through <u>many traumatic stages</u> in their lives — just like teenagers.

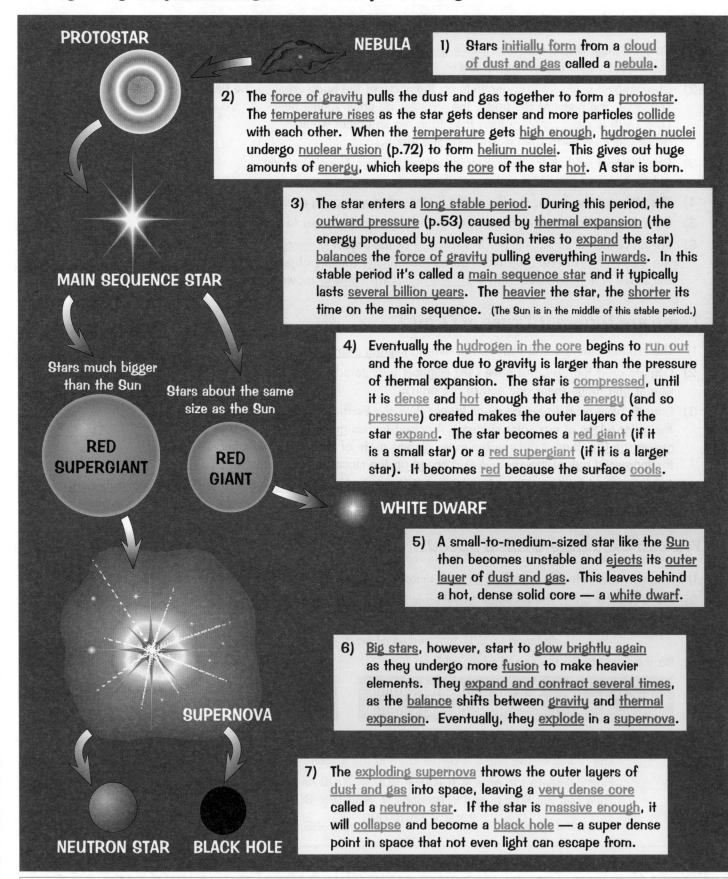

PROTOSTAR

NEBULA

1) Stars <u>initially form</u> from a <u>cloud of dust and gas</u> called a <u>nebula</u>.

2) The <u>force of gravity</u> pulls the dust and gas together to form a <u>protostar</u>. The <u>temperature rises</u> as the star gets denser and more particles <u>collide</u> with each other. When the <u>temperature</u> gets <u>high enough</u>, <u>hydrogen nuclei</u> undergo <u>nuclear fusion</u> (p.72) to form <u>helium nuclei</u>. This gives out huge amounts of <u>energy</u>, which keeps the <u>core</u> of the star <u>hot</u>. A star is born.

MAIN SEQUENCE STAR

3) The star enters a <u>long stable period</u>. During this period, the <u>outward pressure</u> (p.53) caused by <u>thermal expansion</u> (the energy produced by nuclear fusion tries to <u>expand</u> the star) <u>balances</u> the <u>force of gravity</u> pulling everything <u>inwards</u>. In this stable period it's called a <u>main sequence star</u> and it typically lasts <u>several billion years</u>. The <u>heavier</u> the star, the <u>shorter</u> its time on the main sequence. (The Sun is in the middle of this stable period.)

Stars much bigger than the Sun

Stars about the same size as the Sun

4) Eventually the <u>hydrogen in the core</u> begins to <u>run out</u> and the force due to gravity is larger than the pressure of thermal expansion. The star is <u>compressed</u>, until it is <u>dense</u> and <u>hot</u> enough that the <u>energy</u> (and so <u>pressure</u>) created makes the outer layers of the star <u>expand</u>. The star becomes a <u>red giant</u> (if it is a small star) or a <u>red supergiant</u> (if it is a larger star). It becomes <u>red</u> because the surface <u>cools</u>.

RED SUPERGIANT

RED GIANT

WHITE DWARF

5) A small-to-medium-sized star like the <u>Sun</u> then becomes unstable and <u>ejects</u> its <u>outer layer</u> of <u>dust and gas</u>. This leaves behind a hot, dense solid core — a <u>white dwarf</u>.

6) <u>Big stars</u>, however, start to <u>glow brightly again</u> as they undergo more <u>fusion</u> to make heavier elements. They <u>expand and contract several times</u>, as the <u>balance</u> shifts between <u>gravity</u> and <u>thermal expansion</u>. Eventually, they <u>explode</u> in a <u>supernova</u>.

SUPERNOVA

7) The <u>exploding supernova</u> throws the outer layers of <u>dust and gas</u> into space, leaving a <u>very dense core</u> called a <u>neutron star</u>. If the star is <u>massive enough</u>, it will <u>collapse</u> and become a <u>black hole</u> — a super dense point in space that not even light can escape from.

NEUTRON STAR   **BLACK HOLE**

It's the beginning of the world as we know it...

Pretty neat, seeing how stars like our Sun — which all of us rely on — were made all those years ago.

Q1   Describe the life cycle of a star the same size as our Sun, beginning from a nebula.   [6 marks]

Classifying Stars

We need to be able to categorise and compare stars, so we can better understand our universe.

Stars can be Classified by their Colours

1) The colour of a star depends on the visible light it emits. All stars emit visible light, but how much it emits of each frequency depends on its surface temperature.

2) This means we can classify stars based on their colour. We use red, orange, yellow, white and blue. All stars of a similar colour will be of a similar temperature.

3) The hotter the star, the more light of higher frequencies it will emit.

4) A cool star will emit most of its visible light at the lowest frequency of visible light (i.e. red light — see page 28), and so it will appear red.

5) Orange stars are hotter than red stars, yellow stars are hotter than orange stars, and white stars are hotter than yellow stars. White stars emit all frequencies of visible light roughly equally.

6) Blue stars are hotter than white stars. They emit more high frequency light (blue, indigo and violet) than lower frequency ones (red and orange), and so they appear blue.

Colour	Surface Temperature
Blue	Hottest
White	↑
Yellow	
Orange	
Red	Coolest

You can Compare Brightness using Absolute Magnitude

1) A star's brightness depends on its size and temperature. In general, the bigger and hotter the star, the brighter it is.

2) Classifying stars by brightness can be difficult, since the brightness they appear from Earth also depends on their distance from Earth. The closer the star, the brighter it appears.

3) If we just looked at brightness, we may end up classifying stars that are very far away but very bright in the same group as a star that is relatively dim, but nearby, which wouldn't be very useful.

4) To deal with this, we use a value called 'absolute magnitude'.

5) Absolute magnitude is a measure of how bright a given star would appear to be if it was a fixed distance from Earth (around 3.1×10^{17} m). This allows us to compare the brightness of stars without worrying about their relative distances from Earth.

6) Confusingly, the lower the absolute magnitude, the brighter the star. Very bright stars have a negative value for their absolute magnitudes. For example, the Sun has an absolute magnitude of around $+5$, while the Pole Star, one of the brightest looking stars in the night sky, has an absolute magnitude of around -4.

You can See Different Types of Star on the Hertzsprung-Russell Diagram

1) The Hertzsprung-Russell diagram is a graph of absolute magnitude against temperature for many, many stars.

2) There are clear groups on the graph that correspond to different periods in a star's life cycle.

3) Red giants and red supergiants are in the top-right. They are cool, but very large, and so are very bright.

4) White dwarfs are found in the bottom-left. They are very hot, but small, so are dim.

5) Main sequence stars span the whole range of the graph diagonally from top-left to bottom-right. Since all main sequence stars are roughly the same size, the brighter the star, the higher the temperature.

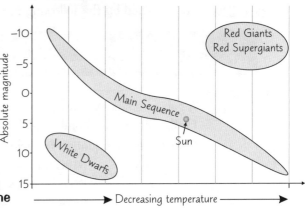

Welcome to Star Class. I've been told you're all pretty bright ...

This stuff's a little tricky. Be careful with absolute magnitude. Remember, the lower the number, the brighter the star.

Q1   Star A is orange, star B is white and star C is yellow. Which star has the highest surface temperature? [1 mark]

Red-shift

When we look at the light we detect from galaxies, everything's <u>shifted</u> from where it should be. Weird.

Waves are Affected by the Motion of the Source

1) As you saw on page 28, when a <u>source</u> of waves is <u>moving</u> relative to the <u>observer</u>, the waves will undergo a <u>change in frequency</u> and <u>wavelength</u> when they are <u>observed</u>, compared to when they were <u>emitted</u> — this is the Doppler Effect.

2) This happens with <u>all</u> types of <u>waves</u>, including <u>light</u>.

3) If the <u>light source</u> is <u>moving away</u> from you, the light it emits will be <u>shifted towards the red end</u> (i.e. the lower frequency end) of the visible part of the EM spectrum — this is <u>red-shift</u>.

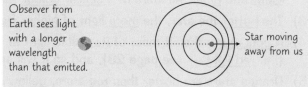

Observer from Earth sees light with a longer wavelength than that emitted.

Star moving away from us

4) Astronomers see this happening with light from <u>stars</u>. The light from distant stars is <u>red-shifted</u> — we observe light with a <u>longer wavelength</u> (lower frequency) than we would expect the stars to emit. The stars must be <u>moving away</u> from the Earth.

Light from Galaxies is Red-shifted

Most <u>galaxies</u> seem to be <u>moving away</u> from each other. There's good evidence for this:

1) Different elements <u>absorb</u> different <u>frequencies</u> (or wavelengths) of light.

2) When light is passed through a sample of an element, a <u>pattern</u> of <u>dark lines</u> is produced — with a dark line at each of the frequencies in the visible part of the EM spectrum that the element <u>absorbs</u>.

An absorption spectrum showing dark lines measured on Earth.

3) When we look at <u>light from distant galaxies</u> we see the <u>same patterns</u> but at <u>slightly lower frequencies</u> (and so <u>longer wavelengths</u>) than they should be.

4) The patterns have been <u>shifted</u> towards the <u>red end</u> of the spectrum — <u>red-shift</u>.

The same absorption spectrum measured from light from a distant galaxy. The dark lines in this spectrum are red-shifted.

Calculating Red-shift

You need to be able to make <u>calculations</u> involving red-shift. The <u>amount</u> that light from a galaxy is <u>red-shifted</u> is determined by the following formula:

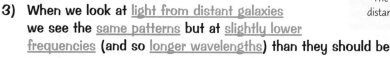

$$\frac{\text{change in wavelength}}{\text{reference wavelength}} = \frac{\text{velocity of a galaxy}}{\text{speed of light}}$$

$$\frac{\lambda - \lambda_0}{\lambda_0} = \frac{\Delta\lambda}{\lambda_0} = \frac{v}{c}$$

The 'reference wavelength' means the wavelength of the light when it was emitted, before it was red-shifted.

Example: A galaxy emits light with a wavelength of 410×10^{-9} m. The light is observed on Earth with a wavelength of 425×10^{-9} m. Calculate the velocity of the galaxy.

Rearrange the equation for velocity:

$$v = \frac{\lambda - \lambda_0}{\lambda_0} \times c = \frac{(425 \times 10^{-9}) - (410 \times 10^{-9})}{410 \times 10^{-9}} \times 3.00 \times 10^8 = 1.0975... \times 10^7$$
$$= 1.10 \times 10^7 \text{ m/s (to 3 s.f.)}$$

The speed of light is 3.00×10^8 m/s.

My brain's shifted towards the tired end of the spectrum...

Red-shift of light affects both wavelength and frequency, since light travels at a constant speed and $c = f\lambda$ (see p.27).

Q1 Calculate the observed change in wavelength of light that is emitted with a wavelength of 550×10^{-9} m from a galaxy that is moving away from Earth at a speed of 2.75×10^7 m/s. **[3 marks]**

The Big Bang

'How it all began' is a tricky question that we just can't answer. Our best guess at the minute is the Big Bang.

Red-shift Suggests the Universe is Expanding

1) Measurements of the red-shift suggest that all the distant galaxies are moving away from us very quickly — and it's the same result whichever direction you look in.

2) More distant galaxies have greater red-shifts than nearer ones — they show a bigger observed increase in wavelength.

3) This means that more distant galaxies are moving away faster than nearer ones.

4) The inescapable conclusion appears to be that the whole universe (space itself) is expanding.

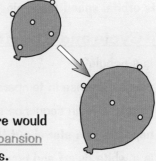

- Imagine a balloon covered with pompoms.
- As you blow into the balloon, it stretches. The pompoms move further away from each other.
- The balloon represents the universe and each pompom is a galaxy. As time goes on, space stretches and expands, moving the galaxies away from each other.
- This is a simple model (balloons only stretch so far, and there would be galaxies 'inside' the balloon too) but it shows how the expansion of space makes it look like galaxies are moving away from us.

There's Microwave Radiation from All Directions

This is another observation that scientists made. It's not super interesting in itself, but the model that explains it definitely is.

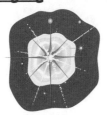

Cosmic maaaaaan!

1) Scientists can detect low frequency microwave radiation coming from all directions and all parts of the universe.

2) It's known as the Cosmic Microwave Background (CMB) radiation.

3) For complicated reasons this background radiation is strong evidence for an initial Big Bang (see below). As the universe expands and cools, this background radiation 'cools' and drops in frequency.

This Evidence Suggests the Universe Started with a Bang

The galaxies are moving away from each other at great speed — suggesting something must have got them going from a single starting point. That 'something' was probably a big explosion — the Big Bang:

1) Initially, all the matter in the universe occupied a single point.

2) This tiny space was very dense and very hot.

3) This single point then 'exploded' — the Big Bang.

4) Space started expanding, and the expansion is still going on.

According to the Big Bang model, CMB radiation is the leftover energy of this initial explosion. Pretty neat, eh?

And it all started with the Big Bang...

The Big Bang model is the best one we've got to explain how the universe began, but it may need some tweaking in the future if we find new evidence it can't explain. Scientists, pfft, don't they ever finish anything?

Q1   How does observed light from distant galaxies suggest that the universe is expanding?   [4 marks]

Revision Questions for Section 8

Well, that wraps up <u>Section 8</u>. Now you've learnt the secrets of the cosmos, time to come back down to Earth and see how much of it is still orbiting around your brain.

- Try these questions and <u>tick off each one</u> when you <u>get it right</u>.
- When you've done <u>all the questions</u> for a topic and are <u>completely happy</u> with it, tick off the topic.

<u>Galaxies, Our Solar System and Orbits (p.74-75)</u> ☑

1) What is a galaxy? How many galaxies are in the universe?

2) What force causes the orbits of moons, planets, comets and satellites?

3) How do the orbits of comets differ from the orbits of moons and planets?

4) The Earth is an average distance of 150 million km from the Sun.
Find its orbital speed (assuming the orbit is circular).

<u>The Life Cycle and Classification of Stars (p.76-77)</u> ☑

5) What is a nebula?

6) What causes the rise in temperature that leads to nuclear fusion in a protostar?

7) What causes a main sequence star to remain stable for a long time?

8) What happens to a star about the same size as our Sun when it begins to run out of hydrogen?

9) What is a white dwarf and how is it made?

10) True or false? The Sun will eventually turn into a black hole.

11) What colour of star has the lowest surface temperature?

12) True or false? The higher the absolute magnitude, the brighter the star.

13) Sketch the Hertzsprung-Russell diagram and label the regions of the graph
corresponding to white dwarfs, main sequence stars, red giants and red supergiants.

<u>Red-shift and The Big Bang (p.78-79)</u> ☑

14) What is red-shift?

15) Calculate the original wavelength of light emitted from a galaxy that is moving away from Earth
at 7.8×10^6 m/s and is red-shifted by 15×10^{-9} m when observed in a lab on Earth.

16) True or false? Very distant galaxies are moving away faster than ones closer to us.

17) What does CMB stand for?

18) Briefly describe the ideas that make up the Big Bang theory.

Experimental Know-How

Pro scientists need to know how to plan and carry out scientific experiments. They also need to know how to interpret and evaluate the data they get from those experiments. Unluckily for you, those pesky examiners think you should be able to do the same — don't worry though, that's what this topic's all about.

You Might Get Asked Questions on Reliability and Validity

1) RELIABLE results come from experiments that give similar data:

   - each time the experiment is repeated (by you),
   - each time the experiment is reproduced by other scientists.

2) VALID results are both reliable AND come from experiments that were designed to be a fair test.

In the exam, you could be asked to suggest ways to improve the reliability or validity of some experimental results. If so, there are a couple of things to think about:

Controlling Variables Improves Validity

1) A variable is something that has the potential to change, e.g. mass.
   In a lab experiment you usually change one variable and measure how it affects another variable.

   > Example: you might change only the mass of a toy car travelling down a ramp and measure how this affects its average speed.

2) To make it a fair test, everything else that could affect the results should stay the same — otherwise you can't tell if the thing you're changing is causing the results or not.

   > Example continued: you need to keep the angle of the ramp the same, otherwise you won't know whether any change in average speed is caused by the change in angle of the ramp or the difference in mass of the car.

3) The variable you CHANGE is called the INDEPENDENT variable.

4) The variable you MEASURE is called the DEPENDENT variable.

5) The variables that you KEEP THE SAME are called CONTROL variables.

   > Example continued:
   > Independent variable = mass of toy car
   > Dependent variable = average speed of toy car
   > Control variables = angle of ramp, position of car release, material on ramp etc.

6) Make sure you think about how you'll control these variables, e.g. you could use a ruler to make sure you release the car from the same position each time.

7) Because you can't always control all the variables, you often need to use a CONTROL EXPERIMENT — an experiment that's kept under the same conditions as the rest of the investigation, but doesn't have anything done to it. This is so that you can see what happens when you don't change anything at all.

Carrying Out Repeats Improves Reliability

1) There will usually be differences between any sets of measurements you take, so you should make sure you repeat your measurements at least three times and calculate the mean (average).

2) Repeats with small differences between them show that your measurements are reliable — that they are similar and can be repeated.

Reliable results — they won't ever forget your birthday...

A typical exam question might describe an experiment, then ask you to suggest what variables need to be controlled. Don't panic, just use your scientific knowledge and a bit of common sense, e.g. if the experiment involves using a Geiger-Müller counter to detect radiation, you know that it's affected by the radiation source and the distance of the detector from the source, so these variables need to be kept constant (if you're not actually investigating one of them).

More Experimental Know-How

Thought you knew <u>everything</u> there was to know about experiments? <u>Think again</u> my friend...

You Might Have to Suggest Ways to Make an Experiment Safer

1) It's important that experiments are safe. If you're asked to suggest ways to make an experiment safer, you'll first need to identify what the <u>potential hazards</u> might be. Hazards include things like:

- <u>Light sources</u>, e.g. if a laser is directed into the eye, this can cause blindness.
- <u>Radiation</u>, e.g. radiation from radioactive sources can cause cancer.
- <u>Fire</u>, e.g. an unattended heater is a fire hazard.
- <u>Electricity</u>, e.g. faulty electrical equipment could give you a shock.

Hmm... why is this laser not working?

2) Then you'll need to suggest ways of <u>reducing</u> the <u>risks</u> involved with the hazard, e.g.:

- If you're working with <u>springs</u>, always wear <u>safety goggles</u>. This will reduce the risk of the spring hitting your eye if the spring snaps.
- If you're using a <u>heater</u> to raise the temperature of something, stand the apparatus on a <u>heat proof mat</u>. This will reduce the risk of starting a fire.

You can find out about potential hazards by looking in textbooks, doing some internet research, or asking your teacher.

You Could be Asked About Accuracy...

1) It's important that results are <u>accurate</u>. Accurate results are those that are <u>really close</u> to the <u>true answer</u>.
2) The accuracy of your results usually depends on your <u>method</u>.

> E.g. say you wanted to estimate the <u>volume</u> of an irregularly shaped solid. Working out its volume by <u>measuring the sides</u> isn't very accurate because this will not take into account any gaps in the object. It's <u>more accurate</u> to measure the volume by submerging the object in a <u>eureka can</u> filled with water. You can then measure the volume of water displaced by the object to get its volume (see p.53).

3) To make sure your results are as <u>accurate</u> as possible, you need to make sure you're measuring the <u>right thing</u> and that you <u>don't miss</u> anything or <u>include</u> anything that shouldn't be included in the measurements.

> E.g. if you're using a eureka can to measure the volume of an object, make sure the object is <u>completely submerged</u> in the water before measuring the volume of the displaced water, or the measured volume will be <u>too small</u>.

...And Precision

Results also need to be <u>precise</u>. Precise results are ones where the data is <u>all really close</u> to the <u>mean</u> (average) of your repeated results (i.e. not spread out).

Sometimes, results are described as precise if they've been taken using sensitive instruments that can measure in small increments, e.g. using a ruler with a millimetre scale gives more precise data than a ruler with a scale in centimetres.

Repeat	Data set 1	Data set 2
1	12	11
2	14	17
3	13	14
Mean	13	14

Data set 1 is more precise than data set 2.

Not revising — an unacceptable exam hazard...

It may interest you to know that you won't just have to write about other people's experiments in the exam. Sometimes you'll be asked to describe how you'd carry out your own experiment and all this stuff about reliability and what-not will apply then too. Ah. From the look on your face, I'm guessing it didn't interest you to know that.

Describing Experiments

Drawing Graphs and Interpreting Results

Processing your data means doing some calculations with it to make it more useful. Once you've done that, you can present your results in a nice chart or graph to help you spot any patterns in your data.

You Should Be Able to Identify Anomalous Results

1) Most results vary a bit, but any that are totally different are called anomalous results.

2) They're usually caused by human errors, e.g. by a mistake made when measuring or by not setting up a piece of equipment properly.

3) You could be asked to identify an anomalous result in the exam and suggest what caused it — just look for a result that doesn't fit in with the rest (e.g. it's too high or too low) then try to figure out what could have gone wrong with the experiment to have caused it.

4) If you're calculating an average, you should ignore any anomalous results.

You Might Have to Process Your Data

1) When you've done repeats of an experiment you should always calculate the mean (average). To do this add together your data values and divide by the number of repeats.

2) You might also need to calculate the range (how spread out the data is). To do this find the largest number and subtract the smallest number from it.

Ignore anomalous results when calculating these.

Example: The results of an experiment show the extension of two springs when a force is applied to both of them. Calculate the mean and range for the extension for both springs.

Spring	Repeat 1 (mm)	Repeat 2 (mm)	Repeat 3 (mm)	Mean (mm)	Range (mm)
A	28	37	31	(28 + 37 + 31) ÷ 3 = 32	37 − 28 = 9
B	47	52	60	(47 + 52 + 60) ÷ 3 = 53	60 − 47 = 13

Bar Charts can be Used to Show Different Types of Data

Bar charts can be used to display:

1) Categoric data — data that comes in distinct categories, e.g. solid, liquid, gas.

2) Discrete data — data that can be counted in chunks, where there's no in-between value, e.g. number of protons is discrete because you can't have half a proton.

3) Continuous data — numerical data that can have any value in a range, e.g. length, volume, temperature.

There are some golden rules you need to follow for drawing bar charts:

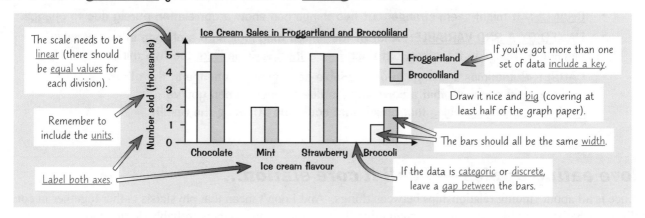

The scale needs to be linear (there should be equal values for each division).

Remember to include the units.

Label both axes.

Ice Cream Sales in Froggartland and Broccoliland

If you've got more than one set of data include a key.

Draw it nice and big (covering at least half of the graph paper).

The bars should all be the same width.

If the data is categoric or discrete, leave a gap between the bars.

Describing Experiments

Graphs can be Used to Plot Continuous Data

If both variables are <u>continuous</u> you should use a <u>graph</u> to display the data.

Here are the rules for plotting points on a graph:

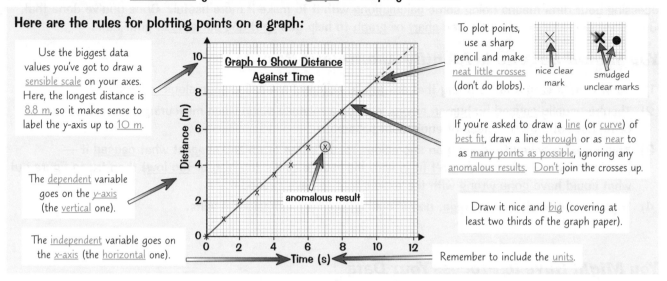

Use the biggest data values you've got to draw a <u>sensible scale</u> on your axes. Here, the longest distance is <u>8.8 m</u>, so it makes sense to label the y-axis up to <u>10 m</u>.

The <u>dependent</u> variable goes on the <u>y-axis</u> (the <u>vertical</u> one).

The <u>independent</u> variable goes on the <u>x-axis</u> (the <u>horizontal</u> one).

To plot points, use a sharp pencil and make <u>neat little crosses</u> (don't do blobs). nice clear mark — smudged unclear marks

If you're asked to draw a <u>line</u> (or <u>curve</u>) of <u>best fit</u>, draw a line <u>through</u> or as <u>near</u> to as <u>many points as possible</u>, ignoring any <u>anomalous results</u>. <u>Don't</u> join the crosses up.

Draw it nice and <u>big</u> (covering at least two thirds of the graph paper).

Remember to include the <u>units</u>.

You Need to be Able to Interpret Graphs

1) A graph is used to show the <u>relationship</u> between two variables — you need to be able to look at a graph and <u>describe</u> this relationship.

> E.g. the graph above shows that <u>as time goes on</u>, <u>the distance increases</u> and that the distance is <u>directly proportional</u> to time.

A relationship is directly proportional if one variable increases at the same rate as the other variable (so if one variable doubles, the other also doubles, etc.). A graph shows direct proportion when the line is straight and goes through the origin (O,O).

2) You also need to be able to <u>read information</u> off a graph. In this example, if you wanted to know the distance travelled after <u>8.2 s</u>, you'd draw a <u>vertical line up</u> to the graph line from the x-axis at <u>8.2 s</u> and a <u>horizontal line across</u> to the y-axis from the graph line. This would tell you that the distance travelled in <u>8.2 s</u> was around <u>7.2 m</u>.

Graphs Show the Correlation Between Two Variables

1) You can get <u>three</u> types of <u>correlation</u> (relationship) between variables:

2) Just because there's correlation, it doesn't mean the change in one variable is <u>causing</u> the change in the other — there might be <u>other factors</u> involved.

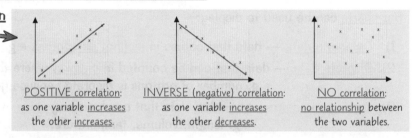

<u>POSITIVE</u> correlation: as one variable <u>increases</u> the other <u>increases</u>.

<u>INVERSE</u> (negative) correlation: as one variable <u>increases</u> the other <u>decreases</u>.

<u>NO</u> correlation: no <u>relationship</u> between the two variables.

3) There are three possible reasons for a correlation:

- <u>CHANCE</u>: It might seem strange, but two things can show a correlation purely due to <u>chance</u>.
- <u>LINKED BY A 3RD VARIABLE</u>: A lot of the time it may <u>look</u> as if a change in one variable is causing a change in the other, but it <u>isn't</u> — a <u>third variable links</u> the two things.
- <u>CAUSE</u>: Sometimes a change in one variable does <u>cause</u> a change in the other. You can only conclude that a correlation is due to cause when you've <u>controlled all the variables</u> that could, just could, be affecting the result.

I love eating apples — I call it core elation...

Science is all about finding relationships between things. And I don't mean that physicists gather together in corners to discuss whether or not Devini and Sebastian might be a couple... though they probably do that too.

Calculating Rates From Graphs

You can work out rates of change using graphs. I bet you can't wait to find out how...

Graphs Can Give You a Lot of Information About Your Data

If you have a graph of distance against time, then the gradient (slope) of the graph will be equal to the speed — the steeper the slope, the faster the speed.

The gradient of a straight line is given by the equation: **gradient = change in y ÷ change in x**

Example: The graph on the right shows the distance travelled by a vehicle against time. Calculate the vehicle's speed.

1) Find two points on the line that are easy to read the x and y values of (ones that pass through grid lines).

2) Draw a line straight down from the higher point and straight across from the lower one to make a triangle.

3) The height of your triangle = change in y
   The base of your triangle = change in x
   Change in y = 32 − 10 = 22   Change in x = 6.5 − 2 = 4.5

4) Use the formula to work out the gradient, and therefore the speed.
   Gradient = change in y ÷ change in x = 22 ÷ 4.5 = 4.9 m/s (to 2 s.f.)

   The units of the gradient are (units of y)/(units of x).

   You can use this method to calculate other rates from a graph, not just the rate of change of distance (which is speed).

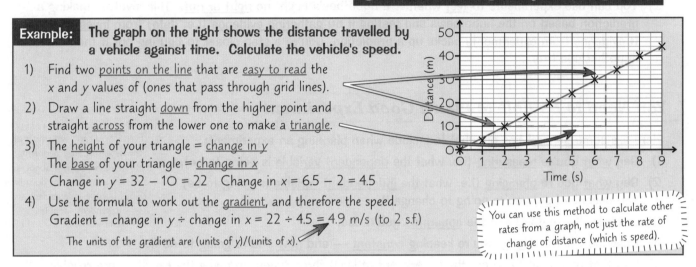

Draw a Tangent to Find the Gradient of a Curve

1) If your graph (or part of it) is a curve, the gradient, and therefore rate, is different at different points along the curve.

2) To find the gradient of the graph at a certain point, you'll have to draw a tangent at that point.

3) A tangent is just a line that touches the curve and has the same gradient as the line at that point.

4) To draw a tangent, place a ruler on the line of best fit at the point you're interested in, so you can see the whole curve. Adjust the ruler so the space between the ruler and the curve is the same on both sides of the point. Draw a line along the ruler to make the tangent.

5) The rate at that point is then just the gradient of the tangent.

Tangent at 40 s.

Example: The graph below shows the velocity of a vehicle, measured at regular intervals. What is the acceleration of the vehicle at 60 seconds?

1) Position a ruler on the graph at the point where you want to know the rate — here it's 60 seconds.

2) Adjust the ruler until the space between the ruler and the curve is equal on both sides of the point.

3) Draw a line along the ruler to make the tangent. Extend the line right across the graph.

4) Pick two points on the line that are easy to read. Use them to calculate the gradient of the tangent in order to find the acceleration (see p.2):

gradient = change in y ÷ change in x
= (22 − 14) ÷ (100 − 40)
= 8 ÷ 60 = 0.13 m/s^2 (to 2 s.f.)

So, the acceleration of the vehicle at 60 seconds was 0.13 m/s^2.

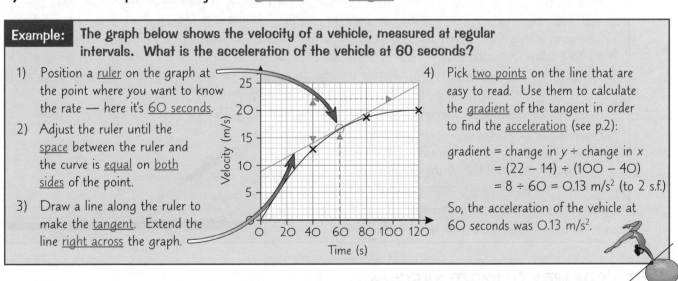

I saw my physics teacher on holiday — he was a tanned gent...

Lots of nifty graph skills here. Gradients aren't too hard, but make sure those tangents don't trip you up.

Planning Experiments

In the exam, you could be asked to <u>plan</u> or <u>describe</u> how you'd <u>carry out</u> an experiment. The experiment might be one you've already come across (easy) or (gasp) you might be asked to come up with an <u>experiment of your own</u> to test something. I know. Examiners are <u>harsh</u>. It's not as bad as it sounds though.

Experiments Test Hypotheses

1) A <u>hypothesis</u> is a possible <u>explanation</u> for something that you've observed.

2) You can use experiments to <u>test</u> whether a hypothesis might be <u>right or not</u>. This involves making a <u>prediction</u> based on the hypothesis and testing it by <u>gathering evidence</u> (i.e. <u>data</u>) from <u>investigations</u>. If <u>evidence</u> from <u>experiments</u> backs up a prediction, you're a step closer to figuring out if the hypothesis is true.

You Need to Be Able to Plan a Good Experiment

Here are some <u>general tips</u> on what to include when planning an experiment:

1) Say <u>what</u> you're <u>measuring</u> (i.e. what the <u>dependent variable</u> is going to be).

2) Say <u>what</u> you're <u>changing</u> (i.e. what the <u>independent variable</u> is going to be) and describe <u>how</u> you're going to change it.

3) Describe the <u>method</u> and the <u>apparatus</u> you'd use.

4) Describe what <u>variables</u> you're keeping <u>constant</u> — and <u>how</u> you're going to do it.

5) Say that you need to <u>repeat</u> the experiment at least three times, to make the results <u>more reliable</u>.

6) Say whether you're using a <u>control</u> or not.

> Even if you can't remember all the details of an experimental method you've learned about, you could still get marks for describing things like the independent and dependent variables.

Here's an <u>idea</u> of the sort of thing you might be asked in the exam and what you might write as an answer...

Exam-style Question:

1 Describe an experiment to investigate the effect of changing the angle of a ramp on the final speed of a toy car released at the top of it. (6 marks)

Example Answer:

In this experiment you should change the angle of the ramp. You can see what effect this has by measuring the average speed of the toy car on a flat section of track at the bottom of the ramp.

Measure the angle of the ramp with a protractor. Set up a flat runway at the bottom of the ramp, then put one light gate near the start of the runway and one light gate near the end of it. Measure the distance between the light gates with a ruler. Ensure the light gates are connected to a computer with data-logging software to record the time taken for the car to pass between them. Hold the car still at the top of the ramp, then let go so that it rolls down the ramp onto the runway. Record the time taken for the car to pass between the gates. Calculate the final speed of the car by dividing the distance between the gates by this time.

Carry out the experiment again with the ramp at different angles (e.g. 35°, 30°, 25° and 20°).

A line should be marked on the ramp to ensure the car is released from the same position each time. The same car should be used each time and the car should not be changed in any way. The same ramp and runway should be used each time.

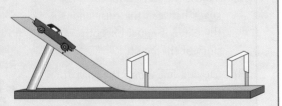

Repeat the experiment three times for each angle of the ramp and calculate an average speed for each angle.

Plan your way to exam success...

The number of marks available for a question like this will vary, but it'll usually be around five or six. This means you'll have to write an extended answer. Think about what you're going to say beforehand and in what order — that way you're less likely to forget something important. Like what it is you're actually measuring, say.

Conclusions and Evaluations

Congratulations — you're nearly at the end of a gruelling investigation — time to draw conclusions and evaluate.

You Can Only Conclude What the Data Shows and NO MORE

1) Drawing conclusions might seem pretty straightforward — you just look at your data and say what pattern or relationship you see between the dependent and independent variables.

A Geiger-Müller counter is set up to measure the count rate a set distance away from a gamma radiation source (see p.68). The table shows the count rate before and after a sheet of paper is placed between the source and the counter:

Obstacle	Count rate in counts per second (cps)
None	15
Paper sheet	15

CONCLUSION: Gamma radiation is able to pass through a paper sheet.

2) But you've got to be really careful that your conclusion matches the data you've got and doesn't go any further.

You can't conclude that every type of radiation can pass through paper — the results might be completely different for other radiation types.

3) You also need to be able to use your results to justify your conclusion (i.e. back up your conclusion with some specific data).

The same amount of radiation passed through to the counter both before and after the paper was inserted, as the count rates were both the same at 15 cps.

4) When writing a conclusion you need to refer back to the original hypothesis and say whether the data supports it or not:

The hypothesis for this experiment might have been that gamma radiation can pass through a paper sheet. If so, the data supports the hypothesis.

Evaluations — Describe How it Could be Improved

An evaluation is a critical analysis of the whole investigation.

1) You should comment on the method — was it valid? Did you control all the other variables to make it a fair test?

2) Comment on the quality of the results — was there enough evidence to reach a valid conclusion? Were the results reliable, valid, accurate and precise?

3) Were there any anomalous results? If there were none then say so. If there were any, try to explain them — were they caused by errors in measurement? Were there any other variables that could have affected the results?

4) All this analysis will allow you to say how confident you are that your conclusion is right.

5) Then you can suggest any changes to the method that would improve the quality of the results, so that you could have more confidence in your conclusion. For example, you might suggest changing the way you controlled a variable, or increasing the number of measurements you took. Taking more measurements at narrower intervals could give you a more accurate result. For example:

Springs stop returning to their original shape when they are stretched past their elastic limit. Say you do an experiment to find the elastic limit of a certain type of spring by taking measurements for applied forces of 1 N, 2 N, 3 N, 4 N and 5 N. The results of this experiment tell you that the elastic limit is at 4 N. You could then repeat the experiment with the same type of spring, taking more measurements around 4 N to get a more accurate value for the elastic limit.

6) You could also make more predictions based on your conclusion, then further experiments could be carried out to test them.

When suggesting improvements to the investigation, always make sure that you say why you think this would make the results better.

Evaluation — next time, I'll make sure I don't burn the lab down...

And that's a wrap. Well, not quite. You've still got the small matter of the whole exam shenanigans to look forward to. Around 20% of your marks will come from being able to describe experiments, and analysing and evaluating data and methods in an appropriate way — so, make sure you're happy with everything in this section. Best of luck.

Answers

Section 1 — Forces and Motion

Page 1 — Velocity and Acceleration
Q1 a) $v = s \div t$
$= 200 \div 25 = 8$ m/s *[1 mark]*
b) $a = (v - u) \div t$
$= (0 - 8) \div 2$ *[1 mark]*
$= -8 \div 2$
$= -4$ m/s^2 *[1 mark]*

Page 2 — Distance-Time and Velocity-Time Graphs
Q1 E.g.

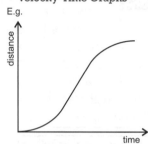

[1 mark for a continuous line that initially curves upwards, and which curves downwards at the end until it becomes horizontal, 1 mark for a straight middle section.]

Page 3 — Mass, Weight and Gravity
Q1 a) $W = m \times g$
$= 32 \times 10$
$= 320$ N *[1 mark]*
b) $W = m \times g$
$= 32 \times 1.6$
$= 51.2$ N *[1 mark]*

Page 4 — Forces and Friction
Q1

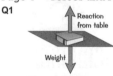

[1 mark for diagram with downwards pointing weight arrow and upwards reaction arrow.]

Page 5 — Investigating Motion
Q1 E.g. it removes human error for timings *[1 mark]*.

Page 6 — The Three Laws of Motion
Q1 0 N *[1 mark]*

Page 7 — The Three Laws of Motion
Q1 The empty trolley has a smaller mass, so less force is needed to cause the same deceleration (and so to stop the trolley) *[1 mark]*.

Page 8 — Combining Forces
Q1 a) If the positive direction is upwards, then the force on the mass is $24 - 20 = 4$ N vertically upwards *[1 mark]*.
b) $F = m \times a$, so
$a = F \div m$
$= 4 \div 2$ *[1 mark]*
$= 2$ m/s^2 vertically upwards *[1 mark]*

Page 9 — Terminal Velocity
Q1 As the object moves faster, the resistance force acting on the object will become greater *[1 mark]*. Eventually, the resistance force becomes equal to the accelerating force, and at this point the object won't be able to accelerate any more *[1 mark]*.

Q2
The open parachute leads to the resistance force equalling the skydiver's weight at a much lower speed than before the parachute was opened *[1 mark]*. This mean's the skydiver falls much more slowly (i.e. has a lower terminal velocity) after they've opened the parachute *[1 mark]*.

Page 10 — Hooke's Law
Q1 It is a straight line through the origin *[1 mark]* until the material reaches its elastic limit. Beyond this point, the graph starts to curve *[1 mark]*.

Page 11 — Stopping Distances
Q1 Any two from:
How fast you're going *[1 mark]* — the faster the vehicle is going, the longer it takes to stop *[1 mark]*.
The mass of the vehicle *[1 mark]* — with the same brakes, the larger the mass of a vehicle, the longer it takes to stop *[1 mark]*.
How good the brakes are *[1 mark]* — worn or faulty brakes will take longer to stop the vehicle *[1 mark]*.
How good the grip is *[1 mark]* — this depends on road surface, weather conditions and the vehicle's tyres *[1 mark]*.

Page 12 — Momentum and Collisions
Q1 First, convert quantities to the correct units:
58 g = 0.058 kg
11.6 ms = 0.0116 s *[1 mark]*
$F = [(m \times v) - (m \times u)] \div t$
$= [(0.058 \times 34) - (0.058 \times 0)] \div 0.0116$
[1 mark]
$F = 170$ N *[1 mark]*

Page 13 — Turning Effects and Centre of Gravity
Q1 Moment = force × perpendicular distance
$= 10 \times 0.85$
$= 8.5$ Nm *[1 mark]*

Page 14 — Principle of Moments
Q1 For moments to balance,
anticlockwise moment = clockwise moment
$= 108$ Nm *[1 mark]*.
anticlockwise moment = force × distance from pivot (d)
so d = anticlockwise moment ÷ force
$= 108 \div 27$
$= 4$ m *[1 mark]*

Section 2 — Electricity

Page 16 — Circuits — The Basics
Q1

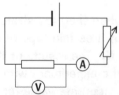

[1 mark for component (shown as a resistor), ammeter, variable resistor and cell or battery connected in a single loop, 1 mark for voltmeter connected across the component]

Page 17 — Resistance and $V = I \times R$
Q1 $V = I \times R$, so
$R = V \div I$
$= 9.0 \div 1.5$ *[1 mark]*
$= 6.0\ \Omega$ *[1 mark]*

Page 18 — LDRs, Thermistors and LEDs
Q1 As the temperature of the thermistor increases, its resistance decreases *[1 mark]*. As the resistance decreases, the current rises *[1 mark]* since the voltage across the thermistor is constant and voltage = current × resistance *[1 mark]*.

Page 19 — Series and Parallel Circuits
Q1 Total resistance, $R_{total} = R_1 + R_2$
$= 7 + 8$
$= 15\ \Omega$ *[1 mark]*
$V = I \times R$, so
$I = V \div R$
$= 12 \div 15$ *[1 mark]*
$= 0.8$ A *[1 mark]*

Page 20 — Charge, Voltage and Energy Change
Q1 $E = Q \times V = 10\,000 \times 200$ *[1 mark]*
$= 2\,000\,000$ J *[1 mark]*

Page 21 — Electrical Safety
Q1 The live wire *[1 mark]*.

Page 22 — Energy and Power in Circuits
Q1 $P = I \times V$
$= 6.0 \times 230$ *[1 mark]*
$= 1380$ W *[1 mark]*

Page 23 — Static Electricity
Q1 As the jumper rubs against his shirt, a static charge builds up on the both the jumper and the shirt *[1 mark]*. This is due to electrons being removed from one and being deposited onto the other *[1 mark]*. The charge becomes large enough for electrons to 'jump' across the small air gap between the jumper and the shirt, causing sparks *[1 mark]*.

Page 24 — Static Electricity and Friction
Q1 E.g. bring the object near the metal disc of a gold-leaf electroscope *[1 mark]*. If the object is carrying a charge, the gold leaf on the electroscope will rise *[1 mark]*.

Page 25 — Static Electricity — Examples
Q1 E.g. photocopier / inkjet printer *[1 mark]*

Section 3 — Waves

Page 27 — Waves — The Basics
Q1 $v = f \times \lambda = (19 \times 10^3) \times (12.5 \times 10^{-2})$
$= 2375$ *[1 mark]*

Page 28 — Wave Behaviour and EM Waves
Q1 The observed frequency of the siren is lower after the ambulance has passed than it was before *[1 mark]*. This is due to the Doppler effect *[1 mark]*.

Page 29 — Uses of Electromagnetic Waves
Q1 Any two from: e.g. electrical heaters / thermal imaging / cooking *[2 marks]*

Page 30 — Uses of Electromagnetic Waves
Q1 E.g. gamma rays are less likely to damage some types of plastic instruments than boiling *[1 mark]*.

Answers

Page 31 — Dangers of Electromagnetic Waves

Q1 E.g. gamma rays are ionising so they can cause tissue damage and cancer *[1 mark]*. They carry more energy than visible light, so their potential for damage is higher *[1 mark]*.

Page 32 — Reflection and Refraction of Waves

Q1 25° *[1 mark]*

Page 33 — More About Refraction of Waves

Q1
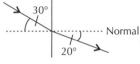

[1 mark for correctly drawn angle of incidence, 1 mark for correctly drawn angle of refraction.]

Page 34 — Refractive Index and Snell's Law

Q1 First calculate n:

$n = \dfrac{c}{v} = \dfrac{3.0 \times 10^8}{1.9 \times 10^8} = 1.578...$

Rearranging $n = \dfrac{\sin i}{\sin r}$:

$\Rightarrow \sin r = \dfrac{\sin i}{n}$

$\Rightarrow r = \sin^{-1}\left(\dfrac{\sin i}{n}\right) = \sin^{-1}\left(\dfrac{\sin 34°}{1.578...}\right)$

$= 20.74... = 21°$ (to 2 s.f.)

[3 marks for correct answer, otherwise 1 mark for calculating n and 1 mark for correct working.]

Page 35 — Refractive Index and Critical Angles

Q1 $\sin C = \dfrac{1}{n} \Rightarrow C = \sin^{-1}\left(\dfrac{1}{n}\right)$

$C = \sin^{-1}\left(\dfrac{1}{1.4}\right) = 45.58... = 46°$ (to 2 s.f.)

[2 marks for correct answer, otherwise 1 mark for correct working.]

Page 37 — Sound Waves

Q1 Sound waves travel faster through denser material *[1 mark]*. The sound moves from air of lower density to air of higher density, so the speed of the sound wave increases as it gets closer to the ground *[1 mark]*.

Q2 $v = f \times \lambda \Rightarrow \lambda = \dfrac{v}{f}$

$\lambda = \dfrac{v}{f} = \dfrac{340}{560} = 0.607... = 0.61\,\text{m}$ (to 2 s.f.)

[2 marks for correct answer, otherwise 1 mark for correct working.]

Section 4 — Energy Resources and Energy Transfers

Page 39 — Conservation of Energy

Q1 mechanically, electrically, by heating and by radiation *[1 mark]*

Page 40 — Efficiency

Q1 Useful energy output = 500 − 420
= 80 J *[1 mark]*

efficiency = $\dfrac{\text{useful energy output}}{\text{total energy output}} \times 100\%$

$= \dfrac{80}{500} \times 100\%$ *[1 mark]*

$= 16\%$ *[1 mark]*

Page 41 — Energy Transfers

Q1 As the ball falls, energy is transferred mechanically from its gravitational potential energy store to its kinetic energy store *[1 mark]*. When the ball hits the ground, energy is transferred away by sound waves *[1 mark]*. The rest of the energy is carried away by heating to the thermal energy stores of the ball, the ground and the surroundings *[1 mark]*.

Q2 Energy in the chemical energy store of the wood is transferred by heating to the thermal energy stores of the surroundings *[1 mark]*. The rest of the energy is transferred away by light *[1 mark]*.

Page 42 — Sankey Diagrams

Q1
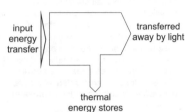

[1 mark for straight arrow to represent energy transferred away by light, 1 mark for downwards pointing arrow to thermal energy stores]

Page 43 — Energy Transfer by Heating

Q1 conduction *[1 mark]*

Page 44 — Convection

Q1 Hot fluid rises because it has a lower density than the cooler fluid surrounding it *[1 mark]*.

Page 45 — More Energy Transfers by Heating

Q1 Black surfaces are better emitters of radiation, so a black mug would radiate energy more quickly than a white mug *[1 mark]*. So energy would be carried away more quickly from the thermal energy store of the water *[1 mark]*.

Page 46 — Work and Power

Q1 Convert energy to J:
$W = 6 \times 1000 = 6000$ J
$P = W \div T$
$= 6000 \div 30$ *[1 mark]*
$= 200$ W *[1 mark]*

Page 47 — Kinetic and Potential Energy Stores

Q1 The change in height is 5 m.
So the energy transferred from the gravitational potential energy store is:
$\Delta \text{GPE} = m \times g \times \Delta h = 2 \times 10 \times 5$ *[1 mark]*
$= 100$ J *[1 mark]*
This is transferred to the kinetic energy store of the object, so KE = 100 J *[1 mark]*
KE = $\tfrac{1}{2} \times m \times v^2$ so $v^2 = (2 \times \text{KE}) \div m$
$= (2 \times 100) \div 2$ *[1 mark]*
$= 100$
$v = \sqrt{100} = 10$ m/s *[1 mark]*

Page 48 — Non-Renewable Energy and Power Stations

Q1 As the coal burns it heats the water in the boiler. The water boils, making steam *[1 mark]*. The steam drives a turbine, which in turn drives a generator, generating electricity *[1 mark]*.

Page 50 — Solar and Wave Power

Q1 Any one from: e.g. some people think wind turbines spoil the view / wind turbines can be quite noisy / you can only generate electricity when it's windy/the electricity supply is unreliable / you can't generate more electricity in response to high demand. *[1 mark]*

Q2 Advantage, e.g. solar power produces no pollution when being used / it has almost no running costs. *[1 mark]*
Disadvantage, e.g. production can't be increased to meet extra demand / solar cells can only produce electricity when there is a certain amount of sunlight / solar cells are expensive to produce. *[1 mark]*

Page 51 — Generating Electricity Using Water

Q1 Advantage, e.g. the electricity supply is usually reliable / you can generate more electricity in response to high demand / it has minimal running costs. *[1 mark]*
Disadvantage, e.g. it has a big impact on the environment / the initial cost is high / you need to flood a valley / it can lead to a loss of habitat. *[1 mark]*

Section 5 — Solids, Liquids and Gases

Page 53 — Density and Pressure

Q1 volume in m³ = 75 ÷ (100³)
$= 7.5 \times 10^{-5}$ m³ *[1 mark]*
density = mass ÷ volume
$= 0.45 \div (7.5 \times 10^{-5})$ *[1 mark]*
$= 6000$ kg/m³ *[1 mark]*

Q2 Pressure = force ÷ area = 49 ÷ 0.044
= 1113.63... = 1.1 kPa (to 2 s.f.)
[2 marks for correct answer, otherwise 1 mark for correct substitution.]

Page 54 — Changes of State

Q1 Particles near the surface of the liquid can escape if they are travelling in the right direction *[1 mark]* and they have enough energy in their kinetic energy stores to overcome the attractive forces of the other particles in the liquid *[1 mark]*.

Page 55 — Temperature and Particle Theory

Q1 25 + 273 = 298 K *[1 mark]*

Page 56 — Particle Theory and Pressure in Gases

Q1 $V_2 = \dfrac{V_1}{3} \Rightarrow \dfrac{V_1}{V_2} = 3$

$p_1 V_1 = p_2 V_2 \Rightarrow p_2 = \dfrac{p_1 V_1}{V_2}$

$p_2 = 310 \times 3 = 930$ kPa
[3 marks for correct answer, otherwise 1 mark for correct rearrangement and 1 mark for correct substitution.]

Page 57 — Specific Heat Capacity

Q1 $\Delta Q = mc\Delta T$, so:
$\Delta T = \Delta Q \div (m \times c)$
$= 1680 \div (0.20 \times 420)$ *[1 mark]*
$= 20$ °C *[1 mark]*

Answers

Section 6 — Magnetism and Electromagnetism

Page 59 — Magnets and Magnetic Fields
Q1 E.g.

[1 mark for correctly drawn lines, 1 mark for arrows drawn pointing towards the poles]

Page 60 — Electromagnetism
Q1 Soft magnetic materials lose their induced magnetism quickly *[1 mark]*, and hard magnetic materials keep their induced magnetism permanently *[1 mark]*.

Page 61 — The Motor Effect
Q1 The first finger is the magnetic field, the second finger is the current and the thumb is the force/motion *[1 mark]*.

Page 62 — Electric Motors and Loudspeakers
Q1 By either swapping the polarity of the d.c. supply *[1 mark]* or by swapping the magnetic poles over *[1 mark]*.

Page 63 — Electromagnetic Induction
Q1 The creation of a voltage in a wire which is experiencing a change in magnetic field *[1 mark]*.

Page 64 — Transformers
Q1 $V_s \div V_p = N_s \div N_p \Rightarrow V_s = (N_s \div N_p) \times V_p$
$V_s = (770 \div 320) \times 65 = 156.4...$
$= 160$ V (to 2 s.f.)
[3 marks for correct answer, otherwise 1 mark for correct rearrangement and 1 mark for correct working.]

Section 7 — Radioactivity and Particles

Page 66 — Radioactivity
Q1 $^{15}_{7}$N is an isotope of $^{14}_{7}$N *[1 mark]*. Isotopes are atoms with the same atomic number (7) but different mass numbers (14 and 15) *[1 mark]*.

Page 67 — Ionising Radiation
Q1 Ionisation is where an electron is knocked off an atom. The atom (which has no overall charge) is turned into an ion (with a charge) *[1 mark]*.
Q2 Alpha, beta, gamma, neutron *[1 mark]*.

Page 68 — Investigating Radiation & Nuclear Equations
Q1 Beta particle *[1 mark]*
Q2 $^{219}_{86}$Rn $\rightarrow$ $^{215}_{84}$Po $+ ^{4}_{2}\alpha$
[1 mark for correct layout, 1 mark for correct symbol for an alpha particle, 1 mark for total atomic and mass numbers being equal on both sides]

Page 69 — Half-life
Q1 After one half-life the activity will be
$40 \div 2 = 20$ Bq *[1 mark]*
After a second: $20 \div 2 = 10$ Bq
After a third: $10 \div 2 = 5$ Bq *[1 mark]*

Page 70 — Uses of Nuclear Radiation
Q1 Alpha radiation doesn't penetrate aluminium *[1 mark]*, so the reading on a detector wouldn't change as the thickness of the aluminium changes *[1 mark]*.

Page 71 — Risks from Nuclear Radiation
Q1 Irradiation is when an object is exposed to radiation from a source. Contamination is when the source itself gets onto the object *[1 mark]*.
Q2 Any three of: E.g. handle sources with tongs / use a robotic arm to handle sources / stand behind a protective/lead shield/in a different room / keep sources in lead-lined boxes.
[2 marks for any three safety measures, otherwise 1 mark for only one measure]

Page 72 — Nuclear Fission and Fusion
Q1

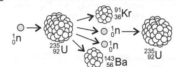

[3 marks for a labelled diagram — 1 mark for showing a neutron being absorbed to cause splitting, 1 mark for a large nucleus splitting into two smaller nuclei, 1 mark for it producing a neutron that is absorbed by another large, unstable nucleus.]
Q2 All nuclei have a positive charge, so when they are close they repel each other *[1 mark]*. High pressures and temperatures are needed to overcome this electrostatic repulsion and fuse the two nuclei together *[1 mark]*.

Section 8 — Astrophysics

Page 74 — The Universe
Q1 The Milky Way *[1 mark]*.
Q2 The gravitational force acts towards the body the object is orbiting *[1 mark]*, which changes the direction of the velocity *[1 mark]*. So the object is constantly changing direction without changing speed and moves in a curved path around the larger object *[1 mark]*.

Page 75 — Gravity and Orbits
Q1 Convert 30 hours to seconds:
$T = 30 \times 60 \times 60 = 108\,000$ s *[1 mark]*
Rearrange the orbital speed equation for orbital radius:
$r = \dfrac{vT}{2\pi} = \dfrac{1400 \times 108\,000}{2 \times \pi}$ *[1 mark]*
$= 2.4064... \times 10^7$ m
$= 2.4 \times 10^7$ m (to 2 s.f.) *[1 mark]*

Page 76 — Stellar Evolution
Q1 E.g. a cloud of dust and gas (nebula) is attracted together by gravity, forming a protostar *[1 mark]*. As the star gets denser, it gets hotter and hotter, until nuclear fusion of hydrogen nuclei starts to happen in its core *[1 mark]*. This nuclear fusion provides an outward pressure to balance the force of gravity, so the star remains a stable size, as a main sequence star *[1 mark]*. When the star runs out of hydrogen to fuse, it will expand and cool, becoming a red giant *[1 mark]*. Over time, the star becomes unstable, and ejects its outer layers of dust and gas *[1 mark]*. This leaves behind a hot, dense, solid core called a white dwarf *[1 mark]*.

Page 77 — Classifying Stars
Q1 Star B *[1 mark]*

Page 78 — Red-shift
Q1 $\dfrac{\Delta\lambda}{\lambda_0} = \dfrac{v}{c}$
Rearrange for $\Delta\lambda$:
$\Delta\lambda = \dfrac{v}{c} \times \lambda_0$ *[1 mark]*
$= \dfrac{2.75 \times 10^7}{3.00 \times 10^8} \times 550 \times 10^{-9}$ *[1 mark]*
$= 5.041666... \times 10^{-8}$ m
$= 5.04 \times 10^{-8}$ m (to 3 s.f.) *[1 mark]*

Page 79 — The Big Bang
Q1 Observed light from galaxies has all been red-shifted *[1 mark]*. This suggests that the light sources (the distant galaxies) are moving away from us *[1 mark]*. Observations have shown that the more distant galaxies are moving away from us at greater speeds *[1 mark]*. This supports the idea that space is expanding, causing the distances between galaxies to increase *[1 mark]*.

Index

Index

PERI42